THE NEW REGISTER OF POLICING RESEARCH

CATHY BIRD

Series Editor:
MOLLIE WEATHERITT

The Police Foundation

Police Foundation books are available from all good bookshops with distribution by Pinter Publishers, c/o Marston Book Services, PO Box 87, Oxford, OX1 4LB.

In case of difficulty or for mail orders, contact PSI/Police Foundation Book Distribution, 100 Park Village East, London, NW1 3SR, (tel 01-387 2171).

British Library Cataloguing in Publication Data

Bird, Cathy
The new register of policing research.
1. Great Britain. Police research
I. Title
363.2'072041

ISBN 0-947692-11-8

Published by the Police Foundation
314/316 Vauxhall Bridge Road, London SW1V 1AA.
Printed by J E C Potter & Son Ltd, Stamford, Lincs.

CONTENTS

ACKNOWLEDGEMENTS

Firstly I would like to thank all the researchers who have contributed to this book. Without them, there would be no register. Also to the Police Requirements Support Unit at the Home Office for their help in funding the gathering of information for the register. I am particularly grateful to Mollie Weatheritt for her patient and thorough editing, and to Ros Davinson and Wini Thomas for their help in typing and organising the register and for their unfailing good humour at times of crisis.

Cathy Bird
Police Foundation 1989

PREFACE

For those who are familiar with the first register of policing research, published by the Police Foundation in 1987, little introduction is needed to this new register. It is a compilation of research projects on policing being undertaken in British universities, polytechnics and research institutions at the present time. I use the phrase, 'present time' flexibly, to allow the inclusion of some projects in which fieldwork has finished and the funding deadlines passed but where the data are still being analysed and the results written up.

The wide range of projects reflects the growing demand by policy makers, the academic community and the public for more information on all aspects of modern policing. It also demonstrates the increasing acknowledgement by senior officers in the police service that good academically sound evaluative studies of police practice are essential to a service mindful of the need for greater efficiency, improved management practices and the demand by the public for greater accountability.

This register includes details of nearly two hundred research projects. Some are large scale projects, involving teams of researchers over two or three years, funded by large grant giving bodies like the Economic and Social Research Council and the Home Office. Some are part-time projects of individual lecturers, some postgraduate theses and some the results of awards from the Police Requirements Support Unit, Home Office to serving police officers.

Entries are listed in alphabetical order of principal investigator. Where there is more than one principal investigator, the project is listed under the person whose name comes first in the alphabet. There are two indexes, a comprehensive subject index and an index of institutions. Subjects covered include police procedures and methods, police organisation and management, training, relations with the community, the history of policing, crime prevention and wider issues in which the police service or officers play a part.

The register is compiled as a source of useful information. It is designed to be well thumbed and well used. If it remains in pristine condition, then it is not doing its job. I hope you find it useful.

Cathy Bird
Police Foundation 1989

PRINCIPAL INVESTIGATORS:	**Dr DAVID ALEXANDER** **Dr GEORGE INNES** **Dr LESLIE WALKER**
TITLE OF PROJECT:	**OCCUPATIONAL HEALTH IN POLICE OFFICERS**
Co WORKERS:	John Dodd Mary Prodger
INSTITUTION:	University Medical School, Aberdeen
ADDRESS FOR CORRESPONDENCE:	University Medical School Foresterhill Aberdeen AB9 2ZD
DURATION:	October 1986 - March 1989
SOURCE OF FUNDING:	Police Foundation £52,560
POLICE FORCES in which research carried out:	Grampian Police

PROJECT SUMMARY:
To investigate sources of stress, their effects and what steps are being taken to deal with them among local police officers.

METHODOLOGY:
Literature search.
Preliminary interviews with a random selection of police officers.
Postal survey using questionnaires, rating scales and inventories.
Analysing questionnaire data.
Selective interviews of approximately 10% of respondents.
Collection of data from the Medical Officer's files and administrative files.
Analysis of interview and other data.
Preparation of final report and recommendations.

PUBLICATIONS available or to be published:
Summary report to be published by the Police Foundation.

PRINCIPAL INVESTIGATOR:	**DAVID ANDERSON**
TITLE OF PROJECT:	**POLICING THE EMPIRE**
Co WORKERS:	David Killingray
INSTITUTION:	Birkbeck College, University of London
ADDRESS FOR CORRESPONDENCE:	History Department Birkbeck College University of London Malet Street London, WC1E 7HX
DURATION:	Summer 1988 -
SOURCE OF FUNDING:	Various small grants
POLICE FORCES in which research carried out:	-

PROJECT SUMMARY:
A collection of essays on the history of colonial policing, dealing with government authority and control from c 1800 to c 1950. This will be the first collective study of colonial policing in a comparative form using a thematic context.

METHODOLOGY:
Original archival research.

PUBLICATIONS available or to be published:

Anderson D and Killingray D	Policing the Empire: government, authority and control 1780-1930, Manchester University Press, (forthcoming)
Anderson D and Killingray D	Policing and Decolonisation: policing, politics and nationalism, 1918-1960, Manchester University Press, (forthcoming)

PRINCIPAL INVESTIGATOR:	**MALCOLM ANDERSON**
TITLE OF PROJECT:	**POLICING THE WORLD: INTERPOL AND THE POLITICS OF INTERNATIONAL POLICE COOPERATION**
Co WORKERS:	-
INSTITUTION:	University of Edinburgh
ADDRESS FOR CORRESPONDENCE:	Department of Politics University of Edinburgh 51 Buclleuch Place Edinburgh EH8 9JT
DURATION:	July 1986 - September 1988
SOURCE OF FUNDING:	Nuffield Foundation £17,947
POLICE FORCES in which research carried out:	Interpol, Metropolitan Police, FBI, DEA, US Customs, US Secretariat, French, Spanish, Netherlands, Swedish National Police

PROJECT SUMMARY:
This study sets Interpol in the context of other global, regional and bilateral arrangements for police cooperation. The pressures for developing police cooperation and for change in existing arrangements are analysed.

METHODOLOGY:
Interviews and documentary sources.

PUBLICATIONS available or to be published:

Anderson M	Policing the World, Clarendon Press, 1989.

PRINCIPAL INVESTIGATOR: GHALEB BANDESHA

TITLE OF PROJECT: CIVILIANISATION IN THE POLICE SERVICE: PAST, PRESENT AND FUTURE

Co WORKERS: -

INSTITUTION: University of Exeter

ADDRESS FOR CORRESPONDENCE: Centre for Police Studies
University of Exeter
Brookfield Annexe
New North Road
Exeter, EX4 4JY

DURATION: October 1988 - October 1989

SOURCE OF FUNDING: Postgraduate funding

POLICE FORCES in which research carried out: Devon and Cornwall Constabulary

PROJECT SUMMARY:
A critical review of the major 20th century developments connected to civilianisation and an examination of the perspectives of the various groups involved; government, staff associations, trade unions.

METHODOLOGY:
Documents and interviews.

PUBLICATIONS available or to be published:
-

PRINCIPAL INVESTIGATORS:	**PETER BARBERIS** **ARNIE SKELTON**
TITLE OF PROJECT:	**POLICE ATTITUDES AND STYLES OF CONTROL**
Co WORKERS:	-
INSTITUTION:	Manchester Polytechnic
ADDRESS FOR CORRESPONDENCE:	Department of Social Science Undercroft Building Lower Ormond Street Manchester, M15
DURATION:	October 1988 - Spring 1989
SOURCE OF FUNDING:	Manchester Polytechnic £1,300
POLICE FORCES in which research carried out:	Greater Manchester Police West Yorkshire Police Cheshire Constabulary

PROJECT SUMMARY:
In 1984 the researchers investigated the attitudes and aspirations of 800 officers across the ranks of the Greater Manchester Police. The project investigated how and why attitudes changed and related the changes to pay changes, public opinion and political interest. A follow up survey is now being undertaken with a comparative element involving three North West police forces.

METHODOLOGY:
Questionnaire of 15% sample (stratified) and follow up interviews of selected volunteers.

PUBLICATIONS available or to be published:

Barberis P and Skelton A	'Police attitudes and styles of control' Police Studies, Winter, 1985
Barberis P and Skelton A	'Loyalty under stress', Police Studies, Fall, 1986

PRINCIPAL INVESTIGATOR:	**JOHN BAXTER**
TITLE OF PROJECT:	**PRIVACY, POLICING AND SECURITY**
Co WORKERS:	-
INSTITUTION:	University College of Wales, Aberystwyth
ADDRESS FOR CORRESPONDENCE:	Faculty of Law University College of Wales Aberystwyth Dyfed SY23 3DB
DURATION:	October 1988 - October 1990
SOURCE OF FUNDING:	Unfunded
POLICE FORCES in which research carried out:	-

PROJECT SUMMARY:
Investigation of the relationship between legal requirements and practice.

METHODOLOGY:
Library based.

PUBLICATIONS available or to be published:

Baxter J	State Security, Privacy and Information, Wheatsheaf, 1989.

PRINCIPAL INVESTIGATOR:	**JOHN BAXTER**
TITLE OF PROJECT:	**STATE SECURITY, PRIVACY AND INFORMATION (Special Branch/MI5)**
Co WORKERS:	-
INSTITUTION:	University College of Wales, Aberystwyth
ADDRESS FOR CORRESPONDENCE:	Faculty of Law University College of Wales Aberystwyth Dyfed SY23 3DB
DURATION:	April 1987 - April 1989
SOURCE OF FUNDING:	Unfunded
POLICE FORCES in which research carried out:	-

PROJECT SUMMARY:
The interrelationship between state security, privacy and police power; and the discretions involved.

METHODOLOGY:
Library based.

PUBLICATIONS available or to be published:

Baxter J	'Privacy and the maintenance of state advantage', Cambrian Law Review, 1986

PRINCIPAL INVESTIGATOR: PHILIP BEAN

TITLE OF PROJECT: SECTION 136 OF THE 1983 MENTAL HEALTH ACT

Co WORKERS: -

INSTITUTION: University of Nottingham in conjunction with MIND

ADDRESS FOR CORRESPONDENCE: Department of Social Policy & Administration
University of Nottingham
Nottingham
NG7 2RD

DURATION: 1986 - 1988

SOURCE OF FUNDING: King Edward VII Trust, Halley Stewart Trust, GLC and the Mental Health Foundation (for 3 projects £103,000)

POLICE FORCES in which research carried out: Metropolitan Police

PROJECT SUMMARY:
A series of three projects looking into the implementation of section 136 of the Mental Health Act 1983. The projects investigate police decision-making and methods of management in implementing section 136, the response of the mental health services and professionals to the people that the police refer, and relationships between the professional groups involved.

METHODOLOGY:
The first two projects have been completed (details are available from the principal researcher). The third involves questionnaires to police who detain mentally disordered persons, and to psychiatrists who admit them to Claybury and Whittington Hospitals, London.

PUBLICATIONS available or to be published:

Bean P — Arrangements for Treatment and Care, MIND Publications, 1989

Rogers A and Faulkner A — A Place of Safety, MIND Publications, 1987

Rogers A, Rassaby E and Faulkner A — A Public Place, MIND Publications, 1988

PRINCIPAL INVESTIGATOR:	**BARBARA BEARDWELL**
TITLE OF PROJECT:	**PUBLIC ORDER PROBLEMS IN HERTFORDSHIRE NEW TOWNS**
Co WORKERS:	-
INSTITUTION:	University of Exeter
ADDRESS FOR CORRESPONDENCE:	Centre for Police Studies University of Exeter Brookfield Annexe New North Road Exeter, EX4 4JY
DURATION:	October 1988 - October 1989
SOURCE OF FUNDING:	Bramshill Fellowship
POLICE FORCES in which research carried out:	Hertfordshire Constabulary

PROJECT SUMMARY:
Analysis of the relative importance of different explanations of public disorder. Assessment of impact of changes in alcohol consumption, public attitudes to police and their authority.

METHODOLOGY:
Case-study comparison of three towns.

PUBLICATIONS available or to be published:
-

PRINCIPAL INVESTIGATOR: **TREVOR BENNETT**

TITLE OF PROJECT: **AN EVALUATION OF COMMUNITY ORIENTED PATROLS**

Co WORKERS: An independent force of field-workers and a market research company

INSTITUTION: University of Cambridge

ADDRESS FOR CORRESPONDENCE:
Institute of Criminology
University of Cambridge
7 West Road
Cambridge
CB3 9DT

DURATION: January 1987 - December 1988

SOURCE OF FUNDING: Home Office £100,000

POLICE FORCES in which research carried out:
Metropolitan Police
West Midlands Police

PROJECT SUMMARY:
The project evaluates citizen contact patrols in London and Birmingham. The research draws on a recent study conducted in Houston and Newark by the American Police Foundation which aimed to reduce fear of crime by implementing citizen contact patrols.

METHODOLOGY:
The two patrol programmes are evaluated using a quasi-experiment research design based on pre-test and post-test measurements from experimental and control groups using crime and public attitude surveys.

PUBLICATIONS available or to be published:
A report for the Home Office has been prepared. The results of the study are to be disseminated through journal articles and other publications.

PRINCIPAL INVESTIGATOR:	**TREVOR BENNETT**
TITLE OF PROJECT:	**NATIONAL REVIEW OF COMMUNITY-ORIENTED POLICING**
Co WORKERS:	Ruth Lupton
INSTITUTION:	University of Cambridge
ADDRESS FOR CORRESPONDENCE:	Institute of Criminology University of Cambridge 7 West Road Cambridge CB3 9DT
DURATION:	June 1989 - May 1990
SOURCE OF FUNDING:	Home Office £75,000
POLICE FORCES in which research carried out:	National survey

PROJECT SUMMARY:
The researchers aim to visit every force in England and Wales to collect information on the current state of community-oriented policing.

METHODOLOGY:
Site visits, questionnaires, interview schedules, collecting documentary material.

PUBLICATIONS available or to be published:
Final report to be completed by May 1990 and to be available on request.

PRINCIPAL INVESTIGATORS: **Dr KEITH BOTTOMLEY**
CLIVE COLEMAN
Dr DAVID DIXON

TITLE OF PROJECT: **LAW, DISCRETION AND ACCOUNTABILITY: THE INFLUENCE OF RULES UPON POLICE**

Co WORKERS: Dr Martin Gill
David Wall

INSTITUTION: University of Hull

ADDRESS FOR CORRESPONDENCE: Centre for Criminology and Criminal Justice
University of Hull
Hull HU6 7RX

DURATION: November 1986 - October 1988

SOURCE OF FUNDING: Economic and Social Research Council
£60,910

POLICE FORCES in which research carried out: Humberside Police

PROJECT SUMMARY:
An investigation of the extent to which the provisions of the Police and Criminal Evidence Act 1984, and its associated Codes of Practice, requiring the police to keep detailed records of the occasions and reasons for the exercise of their discretionary powers, appear to have influenced police activities and decision-making. The focus is upon the early stages of police investigation of offences, including the exercise of powers to stop and search suspected persons, the search of premises and seizure of property and the detention of suspects in police custody.

METHODOLOGY:
Documentary analysis of police records before and after the PACE Act. Observation of police patrol work, case handling, CID and the treatment of suspects. A programme of interviews with police officers of all ranks in the three research sub-divisions.

PUBLICATIONS available or to be published:

Bottomley A K, Coleman C and Dixon D 'Stop and search, search and seizure', paper presented to Police Foundation conferences, 'PACE - How is it working out', Manchester and Newcastle, May 1989

PRINCIPAL INVESTIGATOR: JOHN BRENNAN

TITLE OF PROJECT: ORGANISED CRIME IN THE WEST INDIAN COMMUNITY

Co WORKERS: -

INSTITUTION: University of Exeter

ADDRESS FOR CORRESPONDENCE: Centre for Police Studies
University of Exeter
Brookfield Annexe
New North Road
Exeter, EX4 4JY

DURATION: October 1988 - October 1989

SOURCE OF FUNDING: Bramshill Fellowship

POLICE FORCES in which research carried out: Metropolitan Police and one other

PROJECT SUMMARY:
Examination of non-street crime and the West Indian community, with particular reference to the existence and structures of organised crime, in the form of groups such as the Yardies. Assessment of implications for policing.

METHODOLOGY:
An attempt will be made to see if Ianni's approach as laid down in the book Black Mafia is appropriate. Interviews with police officers and examination of court records.

PUBLICATIONS available or to be published:
-

PRINCIPAL INVESTIGATOR:	**JOHN BREWER**
TITLE OF PROJECT:	**THE SOUTH AFRICAN POLICE**
Co WORKERS:	-
INSTITUTION:	Queen's University, Belfast
ADDRESS FOR CORRESPONDENCE:	Department of Social Studies Queen's University Belfast BT7 1NN
DURATION:	-
SOURCE OF FUNDING:	Unfunded
POLICE FORCES in which research carried out:	South African Police

PROJECT SUMMARY:
The history, development and political role of the South African Police.

METHODOLOGY:
Library, documentary research.

PUBLICATIONS available or to be published:

Brewer J, Guelke A, Hume A, Moxon-Browne E, and Wilford R	Police, Public Order and the State, Macmillan, 1988
Brewer J	'The South African Police' in Johnson S (ed) South Africa, Macmillan, 1988

PRINCIPAL INVESTIGATOR: JOHN BREWER

TITLE OF PROJECT: AN ETHNOGRAPHIC STUDY OF ROUTINE POLICING IN A DIVIDED SOCIETY

Co WORKERS: Kathleen Magee

INSTITUTION: Queen's University, Belfast

ADDRESS FOR CORRESPONDENCE: Department of Social Studies
Queen's University
Belfast
BT7 1NN

DURATION: January 1987 - October 1988

SOURCE OF FUNDING: Economic and Social Research Council
£12,000

POLICE FORCES in which research carried out: Royal Ulster Constabulary

PROJECT SUMMARY:
A study of how routine policing is affected by Northern Ireland's divisions.

METHODOLOGY:
Ethnographic research; participant observation, in-depth interviewing.

PUBLICATIONS available or to be published:

Brewer J and Magee K	Inside the RUC (in preparation)
Brewer J and Magee K	'The problems of an ethnographic study of the RUC', paper presented at University of Edinburgh conference - Sensitivity as an issue in research, 1988.
Brewer J and Magee K	'Sensitivity as a problem in field research', paper presented at University of Surrey, November 1988

PRINCIPAL INVESTIGATORS:	**JOHN BREWER** **KATHLEEN MAGEE**
TITLE OF PROJECT:	**THE OCCUPATIONAL CULTURE OF THE RUC**
Co WORKERS:	-
INSTITUTION:	Queen's University, Belfast
ADDRESS FOR CORRESPONDENCE:	Department of Social Studies Queen's University 24 College Green Belfast BT7 1NN
DURATION:	January 1987 - Summer 1990
SOURCE OF FUNDING:	Economic and Social Research Council, (one year) Department of Education for Northern Ireland (two years) One year unfunded
POLICE FORCES in which research carried out:	Royal Ulster Constabulary

PROJECT SUMMARY:
A study of the world view of men and women within the RUC, with the emphasis on how they see the role they are required to take on.

METHODOLOGY:
Overt participant observation.

PUBLICATIONS available or to be published:

Brewer J and Magee K	'The dual role of the RUC', paper presented at the British Sociological Association Conference, Plymouth, 1989

PRINCIPAL INVESTIGATOR:	**JOHN BREWER**
TITLE OF PROJECT:	**ORAL HISTORY STUDY OF POLICING IN IRELAND AT THE TIME OF PARTITION**
Co WORKERS:	-
INSTITUTION:	Queen's University, Belfast
ADDRESS FOR CORRESPONDENCE:	Department of Social Studies Queen's University Belfast BT7 1NN
DURATION:	October 1987 - May 1989
SOURCE OF FUNDING:	Nuffield Foundation £1,270
POLICE FORCES in which research carried out:	Royal Irish Constabulary

PROJECT SUMMARY:
A study of the recollections by ex-members of the RIC of their life in the force at the time of partition.

METHODOLOGY:
Oral history (in-depth interviewing).

PUBLICATIONS available or to be published:

Brewer J	The RIC, Institute of Irish Studies, (in preparation)

PRINCIPAL INVESTIGATOR:	**MIKE BROGDEN**
TITLE OF PROJECT:	**ORAL HISTORY OF URBAN POLICING BETWEEN THE WARS**
Co WORKERS:	-
INSTITUTION:	Liverpool Polytechnic
ADDRESS FOR CORRESPONDENCE:	School of Social Science Liverpool Polytechnic Walton House Tithebarn Street Liverpool, 2
DURATION:	January 1987 - March 1989
SOURCE OF FUNDING:	Unfunded
POLICE FORCES in which research carried out:	Merseyside Police

PROJECT SUMMARY:
Using interview material with nonagenarian ex-officers, the project provides a personal account of rank-and-file beat policing between the wars - from recruitment to retirement. Supplementary material has been gathered in the form of contemporary cartoons, postcards, comic strips etc.

METHODOLOGY:
Oral historical techniques.

PUBLICATIONS available or to be published:
Manuscript in preparation.

PRINCIPAL INVESTIGATOR: **MARILYN BROWN**

TITLE OF PROJECT: **FAMILIES OF MURDER VICTIMS**

Co WORKERS: Ruth Christie
David Morris

INSTITUTION: University of Liverpool

ADDRESS FOR CORRESPONDENCE: Department of Social Work Studies
Eleanor Rathbone Building
University of Liverpool
PO Box 147
Liverpool, L69 3BX

DURATION: January 1988 - January 1990

SOURCE OF FUNDING: Home Office £20,000

POLICE FORCES in which research carried out: Metropolitan Police
Merseyside Police
Essex Police
South Yorkshire Police

PROJECT SUMMARY:
The project examines the needs of families and others having significant relationships with murder victims. The research is a component of a demonstration project funded by the Home Office through the National Association of Victim Support Schemes.

METHODOLOGY:
Examination of the processes following murder in relation to the needs of families and others, the work of volunteers, the police role, the resources available to answer needs, the policy of significant agencies and departments and the media role.

PUBLICATIONS available or to be published:
Working papers available from NAVSS, Cranmer House, 39 Brixton Road, SW9 6DZ

PRINCIPAL INVESTIGATORS: Professor RAY BULL
Dr RHONA FLIN

TITLE OF PROJECT: CHILD WITNESSES IN CRIMINAL PROSECUTIONS

Co WORKERS: Dr Julian Boon
Anne Knox

INSTITUTION: Glasgow College

ADDRESS FOR CORRESPONDENCE: Child Witness Project
Department of Psychology
Glasgow College
Cowcaddens Road
Glasgow, G4 OBA

DURATION: May 1988 - April 1990

SOURCE OF FUNDING: Scottish Home and Health Department

POLICE FORCES in which research carried out: -

PROJECT SUMMARY:
The project is concerned with all aspects of child witnesses who are involved in criminal proceedings. It has a special interest in researching the most useful and effective ways of interviewing and questioning children. In this regard the experimental work is geared to evaluating a variety of innovative questioning techniques (eg the 'cognitive interview') and comparing and contrasting their performances in relation to less structured forms of questioning.

METHODOLOGY:
In order to obtain as much experimental control as possible the experiments are fundamentally in vitro. However, in view of the subject matter it is very important to incorporate as much ecological validity as possible into the event stimuli and the testing procedures adopted.

PUBLICATIONS available or to be published:
Full list available from the principal investigators. Most recent publications include:

Flin R H, Davies G M, and Tarrant A B — The Child Witness, report to the Scottish Home and Health Department, 1988

Flin R H, Stevenson Y and Davies G M — Children's Knowledge of the Law, (forthcoming)

PRINCIPAL INVESTIGATOR:	**ELIZABETH BURNEY**
TITLE OF PROJECT:	**PUTTING STREET CRIME IN ITS PLACE: A REPORT TO THE COMMUNITY POLICE CONSULTATIVE GROUP FOR LAMBETH**
Co WORKERS:	-
INSTITUTION:	Goldsmiths' College, University of London
ADDRESS FOR CORRESPONDENCE:	Centre for Inner City Studies Department of Social Science and Administration Goldsmiths' College University of London London SE14 6NW
DURATION:	January 1989 - July 1989
SOURCE OF FUNDING:	Various sources including Gulbenkian Foundation, Hilden Trust, Weavers' Company £6,000
POLICE FORCES in which research carried out:	Metropolitan Police

PROJECT SUMMARY:
A detailed analysis of the location and victims of street crime in Lambeth; who commits such crimes and why; and police strategies for prevention and detection, with a view to making recommendations for improving prevention.

METHODOLOGY:
Analysis of crime reports. Interviews with probation officers and victims.

PUBLICATIONS available or to be published:
-

PRINCIPAL INVESTIGATOR: JOHN BUTLER

TITLE OF PROJECT: PUBLIC DISORDER - LEGAL CONTROLS

Co WORKERS: -

INSTITUTION: Wolverhampton Polytechnic

ADDRESS FOR CORRESPONDENCE: 35 Gower Road
Halesowen
West Midlands
B62 9BY

DURATION: April 1985 - June 1988

SOURCE OF FUNDING: Unfunded but some financial assistance from West Midlands Police.

POLICE FORCES in which research carried out: West Midlands Police

PROJECT SUMMARY:
The aim of the research is to examine the law and practice relating to public order with a view to evaluating a number of propositions concerning the nature of public disorder and the ways in which legal controls are enforced by the police, and to make any necessary recommendations for changes in the law.

METHODOLOGY:
The existing law is analysed and reviewed in the light of an extensive literature survey. The nature of public disorder and actual police practice is studied by a literature review and by an analysis of a sample of prosecutions. Arrests and ejections at West Bromwich Albion football ground over a period of three years are also examined.

PUBLICATIONS available or to be published:
Research contained in thesis available on request.

PRINCIPAL INVESTIGATOR: ROY CARR-HILL

TITLE OF PROJECT: THE ROLE OF THE POLICE: A COMPARATIVE AND HISTORICAL ANALYSIS OF POLICE WAVES

Co WORKERS: -

INSTITUTION: University of York

ADDRESS FOR CORRESPONDENCE: Centre for Health Economics
University of York
York
YO1 5DD

DURATION: September 1986 - July 1989

SOURCE OF FUNDING: Unfunded

POLICE FORCES in which research carried out: -

PROJECT SUMMARY:
Investigation of the extent and nature of growth of police forces over the last half-century.

METHODOLOGY:
Documentation from actual sources, of numbers and types of police throughout the world. Assessment of cross-national patterns and of national trends over time.

PUBLICATIONS available or to be published:

Carr-Hill R 'Moral panic, policing and the politics of public order', Howard Journal of Criminal Justice, Vol 25, No 4, November 1986

PRINCIPAL INVESTIGATORS: Dr MICHAEL CHATTERTON
Dr KEN PEASE

TITLE OF PROJECT: BURGLARY PREVENTION DEMONSTRATION PROJECT - ROCHDALE

Co WORKERS: Alan Trickett

INSTITUTION: University of Manchester

ADDRESS FOR CORRESPONDENCE: Department of Social Policy and Social Work
University of Manchester
Manchester M13 9PL

DURATION: November 1985 - April 1990

SOURCE OF FUNDING: Home Office

POLICE FORCES in which research carried out: Greater Manchester Police

PROJECT SUMMARY:
Following on from the guidance of Home Office Circular 8/84 and research findings that crime prevention should have the greatest chance of success when 'targeted' at a localised problem, the project commenced with an agreement between the Greater Manchester Police and the probation service to work together in an effort to reduce the incidence of domestic burglary on a large council housing estate in Rochdale.

METHODOLOGY:
1986: Information gathering exercise involved victim, neighbour and offender questionnaires, analysis of data obtained, generation of preventative initiatives.
1987: Implementation of initiatives.
1987/88: Monitoring and evaluation.
1987-89: Continued collection and analysis of victim data, re-appraisal of initiatives in the light of this, collection and analysis of data on participants in home watch.

PUBLICATIONS available or to be published:
Forrester D, Chatterton M, and Pease K — The Kirkholt Burglary Prevention Project, Rochdale, Crime Prevention Unit Paper 13, Home Office, 1988

PRINCIPAL INVESTIGATOR: Dr MICHAEL CHATTERTON

TITLE OF PROJECT: DIRECTED PATROLLING PROJECT: PHASE TWO

Co WORKERS: Gillian Steward
Paul Bissell

INSTITUTION: University of Manchester

ADDRESS FOR CORRESPONDENCE: The Henry Fielding Centre
Faculty of Economic and Social Studies
University of Manchester
Manchester, M13 9PL

DURATION: May 1988 - May 1990

SOURCE OF FUNDING: Home Office £73,266

POLICE FORCES in which research carried out: Derbyshire Constabulary, Greater Manchester Police, Nottinghamshire Constabulary

PROJECT SUMMARY:
This project is monitoring developments on sites in Derbyshire and the Greater Manchester Police and a sub-division of the Nottingham force. In Derbyshire, particular attention is being paid to the way the data based on crime and incidents is used to identify problems which section officers can address during periods of uncommitted time. In two divisions of the GMP, the research is concentrated on the role of area constables by monitoring how objectives are formulated with supervision using a computerised management information system and how their efforts are evaluated. In the third division, the use of a similar system to focus the work of all personnel is being investigated. In Nottinghamshire, the project has examined the way computer-based management information is used to plan manpower requirements.

METHODOLOGY:
In the Derbyshire study, a computerised analysis of information is being used to assess the quality of the information and its value to patrol officers. In the GMP, area constables are completing activity checklists and have been interviewed about their work and their position in the organisation. In Nottinghamshire key personnel in the change process have been interviewed in depth, planning meetings observed and data used to target the work of those involved in the initiatives analysed.

PUBLICATIONS available or to be published:

PRINCIPAL INVESTIGATORS: **STEVEN CHRISTOPHER**
LESLEY NOAKS

TITLE OF PROJECT: **ASSAULTS AGAINST THE POLICE**

Co WORKERS: Michael Levi

INSTITUTION: University of Wales, College of Cardiff

ADDRESS FOR CORRESPONDENCE: School of Social and Administrative Studies
University of Wales, College of Cardiff
62 Park Place
Cardiff, CF1 3AS

DURATION: September 1988 - September 1989

SOURCE OF FUNDING: -

POLICE FORCES in which research carried out: South Wales Constabulary

PROJECT SUMMARY:
The research is based on interviews with a sample of all persons alleged to have assaulted the police in a recent 12 month period, whether or not they were actually charged with that offence. The objective is to examine those background and situational factors that can best explain the extent and pattern of assaults against the police.

METHODOLOGY:
Interviews with offenders and observational studies of police-public interactions. Records of offenders and questionnaires and reports filled in by police.

PUBLICATIONS available or to be published:
-

PRINCIPAL INVESTIGATOR: Dr NOEL CLARK

TITLE OF PROJECT: QUESTIONING AND MENTAL TORTURE: PSYCHOLOGICAL AND LEGAL ASPECTS

Co WORKERS: -

INSTITUTION: University of Kent

ADDRESS FOR CORRESPONDENCE: Institute of Social and Applied Psychology
University of Kent
Canterbury
Kent, CT2 7LZ

DURATION: October 1988 - October 1990

SOURCE OF FUNDING: Unfunded

POLICE FORCES in which research carried out: -

PROJECT SUMMARY:
To investigate the psychological and legal frameworks which apply to police interrogation internationally, and compare and contrast these with current international law on the use of mental torture in interrogations.
To clarify the notion of 'mental torture.'

METHODOLOGY:
Mostly archival work.

PUBLICATIONS available or to be published:
-

PRINCIPAL INVESTIGATOR: CATHERINE COBLEY

TITLE OF PROJECT: THE ROLE OF THE CRIMINAL LAW IN THE MANAGEMENT OF CHILD SEXUAL ABUSE

Co WORKERS: -

INSTITUTION: University of Wales, College of Cardiff

ADDRESS FOR CORRESPONDENCE: Cardiff Law School
University of Wales, College of Cardiff
PO Box 427
Cardiff
CF1 1XD

DURATION: October 1988 - October 1989

SOURCE OF FUNDING: University of Wales postgraduate studentship

POLICE FORCES in which research carried out: -

PROJECT SUMMARY:
The project examines the criminal law relating to the problem of child sexual abuse, the professional roles, inter-agency cooperation in theory and in practice, the criminal prosecution of offenders, protection of the child victim, sentencing of offenders and the punishment, deterrence or rehabilitation of offenders.

METHODOLOGY:
Library-based, but it is hoped to include some empirical work when considering inter-agency cooperation in practice.

PUBLICATIONS available or to be published:
-

PRINCIPAL INVESTIGATORS:	**LIBBY COOPER** **JAN KIMBER**
TITLE OF PROJECT:	**EVALUATION OF THE NATIONAL ASSOCIATION OF VICTIM SUPPORT SCHEMES RACIAL HARASSMENT DEMONSTRATION PROJECT**
Co WORKERS:	-
INSTITUTION:	Polytechnic of North London
ADDRESS FOR CORRESPONDENCE:	Community Research Advisory Centre Polytechnic of North London Ladbroke House Highbury Grove London, N5 2AD
DURATION:	April 1988 - April 1990
SOURCE OF FUNDING:	Home Office £36,000 for 2 years
POLICE FORCES in which research carried out:	Metropolitan Police

PROJECT SUMMARY:
To evaluate and monitor 3 demonstration projects in Camden, Newham and Southwark for victims of racial harassment.

METHODOLOGY:
Pluralistic evaluation/action research. Statistical analysis, questionnaire surveys, in-depth interviews, group discussions, observation and monitoring instruments.

PUBLICATIONS available or to be published:

Kimber J and Cooper L	Racial Harassment Demonstration Project, Interim Report, National Association of Victim Support Schemes, December 1988

PRINCIPAL INVESTIGATORS: **Det Chief Insp DEREK COULING**
Dr ERIC SHEPHERD

TITLE OF PROJECT: **PROFESSIONAL JUDGEMENT IN DETECTIVES**

Co WORKERS: -

INSTITUTION: City of London Polytechnic

ADDRESS FOR CORRESPONDENCE: Applied Psychology Unit
Department of Psychology
City of London Polytechnic
Old Castle Street
London, E1 7NT

DURATION: October 1988 - ongoing

SOURCE OF FUNDING: Unfunded

POLICE FORCES in which research carried out: Various British police forces

PROJECT SUMMARY:
An examination of the contributing factors which lead to the widely diverse exercise of professional judgements by detectives faced with the same case.

METHODOLOGY:
Empirical and experimental testing; use of multivariate statistical analyses.

PUBLICATIONS available or to be published:
-

PRINCIPAL INVESTIGATORS:	**DAVID COWELL** **JOCK YOUNG**
TITLE OF PROJECT:	**HOMICIDE IN LONDON**
Co WORKERS:	Tom Woodhouse Jim Dunlop (Metropolitan Police)
INSTITUTION:	Polytechnic of Central London and Middlesex Polytechnic
ADDRESS FOR CORRESPONDENCE:	Faculty of Social Sciences Polytechnic of Central London 76/78 Mortimer Street London W1N 7TB
DURATION:	September 1987 - September 1990
SOURCE OF FUNDING:	Unfunded
POLICE FORCES in which research carried out:	Metropolitan Police

PROJECT SUMMARY:
A replication of M Wolfgang's 'Patterns in Criminal Homicide'; a search for patterns in unplanned criminal homicides in the Metropolitan Police District over a ten year period. Looking also at methods of detection in murder cases and the success of different strategies with different types of murder.

METHODOLOGY:
Analysis of murder files held at New Scotland Yard.

PUBLICATIONS available or to be published:

Cowell D et al — Murder in London, (forthcoming)

PRINCIPAL INVESTIGATOR: CHARLIE COXON

TITLE OF PROJECT: A REVIEW OF POLICE SELF-DEFENCE TRAINING

Co WORKERS: -

INSTITUTION: University of Exeter

ADDRESS FOR CORRESPONDENCE: Centre for Police Studies
University of Exeter
Brookfield Annexe
New North Road
Exeter, EX4 4JY

DURATION: October 1989 - October 1990

SOURCE OF FUNDING: Postgraduate funding

POLICE FORCES in which research carried out: -

PROJECT SUMMARY:
Examination of philosophy and ethos of police self-defence training. Analysis of police perceptions of present system. Analysis of techniques to calm down users of force and to assist the regaining of individual identities after operational participation in a group.

METHODOLOGY:
Interviews and questionnaires.

PUBLICATIONS available or to be published:
-

PRINCIPAL INVESTIGATOR: DON CRONIN

TITLE OF PROJECT: THE APPROPRIATE DIVISION OF RESPONSIBILITIES BETWEEN PUBLIC AND PRIVATE BODIES IN THE MANAGEMENT OF TRAFFIC

Co WORKERS: -

INSTITUTION: University of Exeter

ADDRESS FOR CORRESPONDENCE: Centre for Police Studies
University of Exeter
Brookfield Annexe
New North Road
Exeter, EX4 4JY

DURATION: October 1989 - October 1990

SOURCE OF FUNDING: Postgraduate funding

POLICE FORCES in which research carried out: -

PROJECT SUMMARY:
Analysis of costs of various aspects of traffic management. Comparison with projected costs of civilianisation within the police force and privatisation to bodies outside the police force for the same functions.

METHODOLOGY:
Cost-benefit analysis.

PUBLICATIONS available or to be published:
-

PRINCIPAL INVESTIGATORS: Professor GRAHAM DAVIES
BRIAN CLIFFORD

TITLE OF PROJECT: VIDEO TECHNOLOGY AND THE CHILD WITNESS

Co WORKERS: Helen Westcott

INSTITUTION: Polytechnic of East London

ADDRESS FOR CORRESPONDENCE: Department of Psychology
Polytechnic of East London
Romford Road
London
E15 4LZ

DURATION: July 1988 - July 1990

SOURCE OF FUNDING: Police Foundation £3,856

POLICE FORCES in which research carried out: Metropolitan Police

PROJECT SUMMARY:
The project investigates the perceived credibility of testimony given via a video-link (closed-circuit television), and aims to make appropriate recommendations regarding the implementation of such a system, that are compatible with court procedures. The initial experiment is investigating the perceived credibility of children who have actually accompanied a school outing or merely seen a video recording of the visit; can 'jurors' distinguish between the two groups? Further experiments will investigate the mode and style of questioning in relation to the video-link, and the impact of the kind of television picture of the child presented to the jury with regard to the child's perceived credibility.

METHODOLOGY:
A series of experimental studies are planned, utilising video and interviewing facilities at the Polytechnic. Volunteer students, selected adult groups and members of the public will serve as jurors to assess the credibility of testimony provided by local school children of varying ages.

PUBLICATIONS available or to be published:
-

PRINCIPAL INVESTIGATOR: Professor GRAHAM DAVIES

TITLE OF PROJECT: AN EVALUATION OF THE EFFECTIVENESS OF THE LIVE LINK FOR CHILD WITNESSES

Co WORKERS: Julie Wilkinson
Vicky Hobbs

INSTITUTION: Polytechnic of East London

ADDRESS FOR CORRESPONDENCE: Dr J Wilkinson
Department of Psychology
Polytechnic of East London
Romford Road
London, E15 4LZ

DURATION: February 1989 - January 1990

SOURCE OF FUNDING: Home Office £45,000

POLICE FORCES in which research carried out: -

PROJECT SUMMARY:
Selective monitoring of court cases where the video-link is employed with child witnesses. Information gathered on an observational basis on demeanour and coherence of testimony, attitudes of police officers, court officials and social workers regarding effectiveness of the scheme.

METHODOLOGY:
Attendance at court cases and administration of a behavioural checklist prior to and subsequent to child's court appearance. A checklist is also employed to cover child's emotional demeanour during court cases. Questionnaires for social workers etc.

PUBLICATIONS available or to be published:
-

PRINCIPAL INVESTIGATOR: JIM DIGNAN

TITLE OF PROJECT: EVALUATION OF TWO SCHEMES IN NORTHAMPTONSHIRE WHICH AIM TO DIVERT OFFENDERS FROM THE COURTS

Co WORKERS: D Owens

INSTITUTION: Sheffield University

ADDRESS FOR CORRESPONDENCE: Centre for Criminological and Socio-Legal Studies
Sheffield University
430-432 Crookesmoor Road
Sheffield S10 1BL

DURATION: January 1987 - December 1989

SOURCE OF FUNDING: Northamptonshire County Council
University of Sheffield Research Fund

POLICE FORCES in which research carried out: Northamptonshire Police

PROJECT SUMMARY:
The aim is to monitor the effectiveness of and contribute to the development of two schemes in Northamptonshire which seek to divert offenders from the criminal courts. One is a reparation scheme based in Kettering. The other is a social work intervention scheme based in Northampton.

METHODOLOGY:
An action research approach has been adopted with the aim of contributing to the development of the two schemes in addition to monitoring them and evaluating their effectiveness in achieving their aims. A combination of interviews, observation and data analysis is being employed.

PUBLICATIONS available or to be published:
-

PRINCIPAL INVESTIGATOR:	**Dr DAVID DIXON**
TITLE OF PROJECT:	**POLICING ILLEGAL GAMBLING**
Co WORKERS:	-
INSTITUTION:	University of Hull
ADDRESS FOR CORRESPONDENCE:	Centre for Criminology and Criminal Justice University of Hull Hull HU6 7RX
DURATION:	1986 - 1990
SOURCE OF FUNDING:	Not externally funded
POLICE FORCES in which research carried out:	-

PROJECT SUMMARY:
The project includes the historical study of the policing of illegal betting, concentrating on changes in police attitudes to these duties in the early and mid-twentieth century; also the study of contemporary police attitudes to the control of illegal gambling, based on a comparative study of the UK and Australia.

METHODOLOGY:
Documentary analysis and interviews.

PUBLICATIONS available or to be published:

Dixon D	'Responses to illegal betting in Britain and Australia', in Eadington W R (ed) Gambling Research, University of Nevada, Reno, 1988.
Dixon D	Prohibition to Regulation: bookmaking, anti-gambling, and the law 1890-1990, Oxford University Press, Oxford, 1990.

PRINCIPAL INVESTIGATOR: Dr DAVID DIXON

TITLE OF PROJECT: SOLICITORS, POLICE AND SUSPECTS IN CUSTODY

Co WORKERS: David Wall

INSTITUTION: University of Hull

ADDRESS FOR CORRESPONDENCE: Centre for Criminology & Criminal Justice
University of Hull
Hull
HU6 7RX

DURATION: 1988 - 1990

SOURCE OF FUNDING: Hull University Law School £2,235

POLICE FORCES in which research carried out: Humberside Police

PROJECT SUMMARY:
This is a study of the provision and effects of legal advice to suspects at police stations in three sub-divisions of the Humberside Police. Solicitors and their clerks are being interviewed about their experiences of advising suspects and about the arrangements for providing legal advice. This project is being carried out in conjunction with the research on policing in Humberside by K Bottomley et al. Law, Discretion and Accountability, qv.

METHODOLOGY:
Semi-structured interviews.

PUBLICATIONS available or to be published:
-

PRINCIPAL INVESTIGATOR:	**NICHOLAS DORN**
TITLE OF PROJECT:	**DRUG DISTRIBUTION RESEARCH PROJECT**
Co WORKERS:	Nigel South
INSTITUTION:	Institute for the Study of Drug Dependence (ISDD)
ADDRESS FOR CORRESPONDENCE:	Research and Development Unit Institute for the Study of Drug Dependence 1 Hatton Place London, EC1N 8ND
DURATION:	April 1987 - 1990
SOURCE OF FUNDING:	£50,000
POLICE FORCES in which research carried out:	Various, plus NDIU and Customs and Excise

PROJECT SUMMARY:
Preview of literature on drug trafficking, irregular economies, small firms; development of models or types of drug distribution enterprises and their relationship with law enforcement; analysis of law enforcement strategies from literature and discussions with senior personnel.

METHODOLOGY:
Qualitative methods, including interviews with asset confiscation teams.

PUBLICATIONS available or to be published:

Dorn N and South N (eds)	A Land Fit for Heroin, Macmillan, London 1987
Dorn N and South N	'Some issues in the development of drug markets and law enforcement', paper presented at a workshop of the Commission of the European Communities, Luxembourg, mimeo pp 20.
Dorn N and South N	Policing the Drug Distribution Business, Routledge, (forthcoming)
Dorn N and South N	Drug Markets and Law Enforcement (under consideration)

PRINCIPAL INVESTIGATOR:	**NICHOLAS DORN**
TITLE OF PROJECT:	**FAMILIES REFERRAL PROJECT - NATIONAL DEMONSTRATION PROJECT**
Co WORKERS:	Nigel South Karim Murji
INSTITUTION:	Institute for the Study of Drug Dependence (ISDD)
ADDRESS FOR CORRESPONDENCE:	Research and Development Unit Institute for the Study of Drug Dependence 1 Hatton Place London, EC1N 8ND
DURATION:	1986 - 1989
SOURCE OF FUNDING:	£43,000 with possible extension from a charitable trust
POLICE FORCES in which research carried out:	Metropolitan Police, Merseyside Police, Devon and Cornwall Constabulary

PROJECT SUMMARY:
To explore the feasibility and utility of parents of minor drug offenders being routinely referred by police to local drugs advice agencies. A variety of referral sheets are being tried out in the pilot areas, 1988/9.

PUBLICATIONS available or to be published:

Dorn N and South N	'Drugs and leisure, prohibition and pleasure: from subcultures to drugalogue', in Rojek C (ed), Leisure for Leisure: critical essays, Macmillan, 1987.
Dorn N, James C and South N	'The rise and fall of family support groups', Druglink, ISDD, Vol 3, Issue 1, 1988
Dorn N, Murji K and South N	Referring Relatives: prospects and problems in an inter-agency initiative, (forthcoming)

PRINCIPAL INVESTIGATOR: LIZANNE DOWDS

TITLE OF PROJECT: THE BCS AND CRIME PREVENTION

Co WORKERS: Pat Mayhew

INSTITUTION: Research and Planning Unit, Home Office

ADDRESS FOR CORRESPONDENCE: Research and Planning Unit
Home Office
50 Queen Anne's Gate
London
SW1H 9AT

DURATION: - October 1989

SOURCE OF FUNDING: Home Office

POLICE FORCES in which research carried out: National sample

PROJECT SUMMARY:
An analysis of questions within the 1988 BCS concerning household and vehicle security.

METHODOLOGY:
Victim survey.

PUBLICATIONS available or to be published:
Report to be published in the Home Office Research Study series.

PRINCIPAL INVESTIGATOR: **LIZANNE DOWDS**

TITLE OF PROJECT: **THE BCS AND NEIGHBOURHOOD WATCH**

Co WORKERS: Pat Mayhew
David Elliott

INSTITUTION: Research and Planning Unit, Home Office

ADDRESS FOR CORRESPONDENCE: Research and Planning Unit
Home Office
50 Queen Anne's Gate
London
SW1H 9AT

DURATION: - June 1989

SOURCE OF FUNDING: Home Office

POLICE FORCES in which research carried out: National sample

PROJECT SUMMARY:
An analysis of the neighbourhood watch component in the 1988 BCS.

METHODOLOGY:
Victim survey.

PUBLICATIONS available or to be published:
Mayhew P, Elliott D and Dowds L — The 1988 British Crime Survey, Home Office Research Study No 111, London, HMSO, 1989.

PRINCIPAL INVESTIGATOR:	**Dr D H DUCKWORTH**
TITLE OF PROJECT	**A STUDY OF THE NATURE AND EFFECTS OF INCIDENTS INDUCING TRAUMA IN POLICE OFFICERS**
Co WORKERS:	J Binns
INSTITUTION:	University of Leeds
ADDRESS FOR CORRESPONDENCE:	Human Resources Research Unit Department of Management Studies University of Leeds Leeds LS2 9JT
DURATION:	November 1986 - October 1989
SOURCE OF FUNDING:	Home Office
POLICE FORCES in which research carried out:	West Yorkshire Police Metropolitan Police

PROJECT SUMMARY:
Using retrospective interviews with officers who have been involved in traumatic incidents, the long term study of new cases as they arise, and extensive computer assisted literature searches, the project seeks to improve understanding of the person/situation dynamics involved in the genesis of post-traumatic stress reactions and develop guidance material for managers and professional helpers.

METHODOLOGY:
Analysis and evaluation of psychometric and structured interview material derived from a series of cases.

PUBLICATIONS available or to be published:

Duckworth D H	'Psychological problems arising from disaster work', Stress Medicine, 214, 4, 1986, 315-23

PRINCIPAL INVESTIGATOR:	Professor D DUNKERLEY
TITLE OF PROJECT:	**CAUSES AND CONSEQUENCES OF LABOUR TURNOVER AMONGST POLICEWOMEN**
Co WORKERS:	L Bryant G Kelland
INSTITUTION:	Polytechnic of the South West
ADDRESS FOR CORRESPONDENCE:	Faculty of Social Science Polytechnic of the South West Plymouth PL4 8AA
DURATION:	July 1984 - July 1987 Writing up still underway
SOURCE OF FUNDING:	Leverhulme Trust (1984-1986) Plymouth Polytechnic (1987)
POLICE FORCES in which research carried out:	2 provincial forces

PROJECT SUMMARY:
To investigate the causes and consequences of the high turnover rate amongst policewomen using mailed questionnaires and in-depth interviews. The study looks at the status and role of female officers and considers ways of retaining them and getting them to return to work after absences due to childbirth.

METHODOLOGY:
Postal questionnaires to every WPC in the two forces.
In-depth personal interviews with 10% of WPCs in the two forces.
In-depth interviews with small sample of male officers.
Random interviews with senior women officers nationwide.

PUBLICATIONS available or to be published:
Report submitted to Leverhulme Trust.
Book in preparation.

PRINCIPAL INVESTIGATOR:	**Dr SUSAN EDWARDS**
TITLE OF PROJECT:	**PROSTITUTION, POLICING AND THE WELFARE OF YOUNG WOMEN**
Co WORKERS:	Gary Armstrong
INSTITUTION:	Ealing College of Higher Education
ADDRESS FOR CORRESPONDENCE:	Department of Law Ealing College St Mary's Road Ealing London, W5
DURATION:	March 1987 - August 1988
SOURCE OF FUNDING	Nuffield Foundation £3,000
POLICE FORCES in which research carried out:	Metropolitan Police West Midlands Police Hamburg Police Amsterdam Police

PROJECT SUMMARY:
The study examines the law, policing and the experiences of prostitute women in London focusing on the welfare of young women who are without housing and income and often turn to prostitution to sustain a drug habit.

METHODOLOGY:
Interviews with the street offences squads and prostitute women together with the consultation of police records on arrests and cautions. The study also looked at the effectiveness of recent kerb crawling legislation in England and Wales.

PUBLICATIONS available or to be published:

Edwards S	Prostitution, policing, employment and the welfare of young women, report to the Nuffield Foundation, 1988
Edwards S and Armstrong G	'Policing street prostitution', Police Journal, July 1988
Edwards S	'Red Lights and Red Faces', Police Review, Vol 96, 4968, July 1988

PRINCIPAL INVESTIGATOR: Dr SUSAN EDWARDS

TITLE OF PROJECT: EVALUATING THE IMPACT OF THE FORCE ORDER ON DOMESTIC DISPUTES

Co WORKERS: Lyn Brady

INSTITUTION: Polytechnic of Central London

ADDRESS FOR CORRESPONDENCE: Department of Social Sciences
Polytechnic of Central London
76-78 Mortimer Street
London
W1N 7TB

DURATION: March 1988 - June 1989

SOURCE OF FUNDING: Police Foundation £2,000

POLICE FORCES in which research carried out: Metropolitan Police

PROJECT SUMMARY:
On 24 June 1987 the Metropolitan Police introduced a new force order on domestic disputes requiring officers to regard assault in the home as seriously as assault in the street. The order emphasised the importance of arrest, adequate support to the victim and follow-up services. An evaluation study has been conducted at two stations in London to establish how far the policy is being implemented and what impact the policy has had on deterring violence and enhancing the protection of victims.

METHODOLOGY:
Two stations in the London area have been chosen for study. All records including computer aided despatches, crime books, custody records and incident report books are consulted for a period of six months at each location. The study benefits from an earlier data base collected prior to the force order in 1984-5 at each locality.

PUBLICATIONS available or to be published:

Edwards S — Women, Policing and the State, Sage, (forthcoming)

Edwards S — Report to the Police Foundation.

PRINCIPAL INVESTIGATOR: HADYN ELLIS

TITLE OF PROJECT: COMPUTER FACIAL COMPOSITES

Co WORKERS: -

INSTITUTION: University of Wales, College of Cardiff

ADDRESS FOR CORRESPONDENCE: School of Psychology
University of Wales, College of Cardiff
Cardiff
CF1 3YG

DURATION: 1989 -

SOURCE OF FUNDING: Unfunded

POLICE FORCES in which research carried out: -

PROJECT SUMMARY:
Investigation of the efficiency of Mac-a-Mug (Pro) - commercial software from Sherherezan to produce line drawing faces that can be easily manipulated. Work uses Apple Macintosh II hardware.

METHODOLOGY:
Comparison of Mac-a-Mug with photofit/verbal recall of faces.

PUBLICATIONS available or to be published:
-

PRINCIPAL INVESTIGATORS:	**Det Sgt GRAHAM EVANS** **Dr ERIC SHEPHERD**
TITLE OF PROJECT:	**TALKING TO CHILDREN**
Co WORKERS:	Ms Nadine Eisenberg
INSTITUTION:	City of London Polytechnic Merseyside Police Interview Development Unit
ADDRESS FOR CORRESPONDENCE:	Centre for Research and Development Department of Psychology City of London Polytechnic Old Castle Street London, E1 7NT
DURATION:	February 1988 - ongoing
SOURCE OF FUNDING:	Unfunded
POLICE FORCES in which research carried out:	Merseyside Police

PROJECT SUMMARY:
The aim is to examine empirically the characteristic patterns and problems of investigators talking to children with the purpose of establishing 'facts of the matter'.

METHODOLOGY:
Empirical testing of police interviewers faced with interviewing a child of a given age. Fine grain analysis of video and audio recorded materials arising from these interviews.

PUBLICATIONS available or to be published:

Shepherd E, Evans G and Eisenberg N	Talking to Children (forthcoming)
Shepherd E	'Telling experiences: conversations with child victims', paper presented at BPS Conference, University of Sussex, 1987
Shepherd E	'Getting a child to tell', Police Review, 95, 1080-81, 1987

PRINCIPAL INVESTIGATOR: **HELEN FENWICK**

TITLE OF PROJECT: **THE POLICE AND CRIMINAL EVIDENCE ACT**

Co WORKERS: -

INSTITUTION: Durham University

ADDRESS FOR CORRESPONDENCE: Department of Law
Durham University
50 North Bailey
Durham
DH1 3ET

DURATION: June 1988 -

SOURCE OF FUNDING: Unfunded

POLICE FORCES in which research carried out: -

PROJECT SUMMARY:
Consideration of the recent case law on the Act and the interpretation given to certain provisions.

METHODOLOGY:
Case-noting based on law reports plus synthesising a number of cases to create a longer discreet piece.

PUBLICATIONS available or to be published:

Fenwick H — 'Access to legal advice in police custody: A fundamental right?', Modern Law Review, January 1989

PRINCIPAL INVESTIGATOR: Dr NIGEL FIELDING

TITLE OF PROJECT: COMMUNITY POLICING

Co WORKERS: Jane Fielding
Charles Kemp
Clive Norris

INSTITUTION: University of Surrey

ADDRESS FOR CORRESPONDENCE: Department of Sociology
University of Surrey
Guildford
GU2 5XH

DURATION: 1 November 1985 - October 1987.

SOURCE OF FUNDING: Economic and Social Research Council
£65,000 (plus University contributions)

POLICE FORCES in which research carried out: Metropolitan Police
Surrey Constabulary

PROJECT SUMMARY:
A comparison of relief and permanent beat policing, with special attention to criteria of competence in practice.

METHODOLOGY:
Observation of patrol (statistical and qualitative analysis).
Interviews with police of all ranks.
Documentary analysis.

PUBLICATIONS available or to be published:

Fielding N G — 'Police culture and police practice', in Weatheritt M (ed), Police research: some future prospects, Gower, 1989

Norris C A — 'Avoiding trouble', in Weatheritt M (ed), Police research: some future prospects, Gower, 1989

Fielding N G — The police and social conflict, Athlone, (under commission for publication in 1989)

Fielding N G, Kemp C and Norris C A — Disputes and the police, (in draft)

PRINCIPAL INVESTIGATORS: Dr NIGEL FIELDING
JANE TUNSTILL

TITLE OF PROJECT: JOINT POLICE/SOCIAL SERVICES INTERVIEWS IN CHILD SEXUAL ABUSE CASES

Co WORKERS: Sue Conroy

INSTITUTION: University of Surrey

ADDRESS FOR CORRESPONDENCE: Department of Sociology
University of Surrey
Guildford
GU2 5XH

DURATION: October 1987 - January 1991

SOURCE OF FUNDING: Police Foundation (1987-88) £14,000
Economic and Social Research Council (1988-1991)

POLICE FORCES in which research carried out: 1987-88: Surrey Constabulary
1988-1991: National survey of all police forces in England and Wales, observation in Metropolitan Police and Surrey Constabulary

PROJECT SUMMARY:
An evaluation of joint working between police and social workers in child sexual abuse cases (stages I and II) and a national survey of current arrangements in such cases (stage II).

METHODOLOGY:
Stage I: Observation
Interviews with CSA team
Video analysis.
Stage II: As above, plus CATI (computer assisted telephone interviewing).

PUBLICATIONS available or to be published:
Conroy S, Fielding N G and Tunstill J — Investigating Child Abuse: the study of a joint initiative, Police Foundation, (forthcoming)
Interim report available from the researchers, Department of Sociology, Surrey University, Guildford, GU2 5XH.

PRINCIPAL INVESTIGATOR:	**SIMON FOLKARD**
TITLE OF PROJECT:	**SHIFTWORK AND BODY RHYTHMS**
Co WORKERS:	Peter Totterdell
INSTITUTION:	University of Sheffield
ADDRESS FOR CORRESPONDENCE:	MRC/ESRC Social and Applied Psychology Unit Department of Psychology University of Sheffield Sheffield, S10 2TN
DURATION:	1 October 1987 -
SOURCE OF FUNDING:	Medical Research Council £65,000 per annum
POLICE FORCES in which research carried out:	Surrey Constabulary Sussex Police West Yorkshire Police

PROJECT SUMMARY:
The main aim is to improve shift systems taking account of the characteristics of our 'body clock' with a view to reducing both the individual and organisational problems associated with shift work.

METHODOLOGY
A wide range of methodologies ranging from brief survey questionnaires to detailed sleep diaries to measure body-rhythms and performance efficiency.

PUBLICATIONS available or to be published:

Folkard S and Akerstedt S T	'Towards the prediction of alertness on abnormal sleep/wake schedules', in Coblentz A (ed), Vigilance and Performance in Automatized Systems, Kluwer (forthcoming)
Folkard S	'Circadian rhythms and shift work: adjustment or masking?', in Hekkens W, Kierkhof G and Rietueld W (eds) Trends in Chronobiology, Pergamon Press, 1988

PRINCIPAL INVESTIGATOR: CHRISTOPHER GANE

TITLE OF PROJECT:
a) LAW OF THEFT AND RELATED OFFENCES IN SCOTLAND
b) SEXUAL OFFENCES

Co WORKERS: -

INSTITUTION: University of Lancaster

ADDRESS FOR CORRESPONDENCE:
Department of Law
University of Lancaster
Lancaster
LA1 4YN

DURATION:
1) April 1989 - July 1989
2) May 1989 - July 1989

SOURCE OF FUNDING: Unfunded

POLICE FORCES in which research carried out: -

PROJECT SUMMARY:
In both cases to carry out an analysis of current law regulating topics in question.

METHODOLOGY
Literature analysis, primary sources analysis.

PUBLICATIONS available or to be published:
Both projects are directed towards publication in a series of monographs to be published by Butterworth & Co.

PRINCIPAL INVESTIGATOR: BILL GENT

TITLE OF PROJECT: DESIGNING OUT CRIME IN PETERBOROUGH

Co WORKERS: -

INSTITUTION: University of Exeter

ADDRESS FOR CORRESPONDENCE: Centre for Police Studies
University of Exeter
Brookfield Annexe
New North Road
Exeter, EX4 4JY

DURATION: October 1988 - October 1989

SOURCE OF FUNDING: -

POLICE FORCES in which research carried out: Cambridgeshire Constabulary

PROJECT SUMMARY:
A comparison of two adjacent public housing estates in Peterborough, to see if vastly differing crime rates can be explained by design factors or by age mix.

METHODOLOGY:
Statistical data gathering and architectural study.

PUBLICATIONS available or to be published:
A Brookfield Paper will be published in January 1990.

PRINCIPAL INVESTIGATOR: TERRY GILLESPIE

TITLE OF PROJECT: RAPE CRISIS LINES AND THE POLICE: AN ANALYSIS OF INTER-AGENCY RELATIONSHIPS BETWEEN VOLUNTARY AND STATUTORY SECTORS

Co WORKERS: -

INSTITUTION: Portsmouth Polytechnic

ADDRESS FOR CORRESPONDENCE: School of Social and Historical Studies
Portsmouth Polytechnic
Milldam
Burnaby Road
Portsmouth, P01 3AS

DURATION: 1988 - 1992

SOURCE OF FUNDING: Postgraduate fees paid by Portsmouth Polytechnic

POLICE FORCES in which research carried out: 3 police forces

PROJECT SUMMARY:
The project examines the organisational relationship between Rape Crisis Lines and the local statutory and voluntary agencies with which they are in contact, in particular the police and victim support schemes. Given Home Office guidelines about inter-agency working, together with their commitment to victim support schemes, a key focus is on the implications for the funding of rape crisis lines.

METHODOLOGY:
A combination of formal closed and open-ended questionnaires, interviews and attendance at appropriate meetings.

PUBLICATIONS available or to be published:
Proposal pending for publication.
Co-editing and writing a chapter on women working in local statutory and voluntary organisations.

PRINCIPAL INVESTIGATOR: PAUL GORMAN

TITLE OF PROJECT: POLICE AND POLITICAL ORDER IN INDIA

Co WORKERS: -

INSTITUTION: Hull University

ADDRESS FOR CORRESPONDENCE: Research Services Department
Humberside Police
Bond Street
Hull
HU1 3EN

DURATION: October 1988 - June 1991

SOURCE OF FUNDING: 20% self, 80% Home Office

POLICE FORCES in which research carried out: Indian National Police Academy

PROJECT SUMMARY:
The project seeks to answer the question, 'How is political order maintained in India despite an increasingly authoritarian and politicised police service?', by examining accountability, fiscal control and the use of finance by the Indian Police Service.

METHODOLOGY:
Review of all current literature.
Fieldwork in India - mainly at the National Police Academy, Hyderabad.
Interviews with members of the Indian Police Service.
Analysis of the fiscal data collected.

PUBLICATIONS available or to be published:
-

PRINCIPAL INVESTIGATOR: SIMON GRANTHAM

TITLE OF PROJECT: MOTOR FIT

Co WORKERS: -

INSTITUTION: Dorset Police

ADDRESS FOR CORRESPONDENCE: Organisation & Planning Department
Dorset Police Headquarters
Winfrith
Dorset
DT2 8DZ

DURATION: April 1988 - July 1989

SOURCE OF FUNDING: Home Office PRSU £27,500

POLICE FORCES in which research carried out: Dorset Police

PROJECT SUMMARY:
To develop a prototype system for identifying motor cars used in crime from eyewitness accounts. A colour photograph album of cars stored on computer will be created with the witness gaining access to a shortlist of photographs via indices of verbal descriptions, overall shape and specific features.

PUBLICATIONS available or to be published:
Details of publications available from the principal researcher.

PRINCIPAL INVESTIGATOR: DENNIS GREEN

TITLE OF PROJECT: AN EVALUATION OF THE SOCIAL SKILLS OF POLICING, ITS PHILOSOPHY AND EFFECTIVENESS

Co WORKERS: -

INSTITUTION: Newcastle Polytechnic

ADDRESS FOR CORRESPONDENCE: Faculty of Social Science
Newcastle Polytechnic
Newcastle upon Tyne
NE7 7XA

DURATION: January 1985 - July 1988

SOURCE OF FUNDING: Northumbria Police

POLICE FORCES in which research carried out: Central Planning Unit
District Police Training Centres
Northumbria Police

PROJECT SUMMARY:
A study of the philosophy and development of social skills training in police initial training, and an evaluation of its effectiveness.

METHODOLOGY:
An examination of documentary sources, an analysis of pre and post course questionnaires in 1985 and 1988.

PUBLICATIONS available or to be published:
-

PRINCIPAL INVESTIGATOR: CHRISTOPHER HALE

TITLE OF PROJECT: BRITISH CRIME SURVEYS: A COMPARATIVE STUDY OF SOME NATIONAL AND LOCAL DATA SETS

Co WORKERS: Patricia Pack
John Salkeld

INSTITUTION: University of Kent

ADDRESS FOR CORRESPONDENCE: Rutherford College
University of Kent
Canterbury
Kent
CT2 7NX

DURATION: October 1988 - September 1990

SOURCE OF FUNDING: Economic and Social Research Council
£28,700

POLICE FORCES in which research carried out: -

PROJECT SUMMARY:
A comparative study of the 1982 and 1984 British Crime Surveys and the Merseyside and Islington local crime surveys with particular reference to fear of crime, victimisation, perceptions of police and attitudes to punishment.

METHODOLOGY:
Statistical analysis including LISREL, logit and correspondence analysis.

PUBLICATIONS available or to be published:
-

PRINCIPAL INVESTIGATOR: **CHRISTOPHER HAMMOND**

TITLE OF PROJECT: **IDEOLOGY AND CONSENSUS, AN EXAMINATION OF THE CIVIL AND MILITARY POLICING OF PALESTINE FROM 1920-1936**

Co WORKERS: -

INSTITUTION: Birkbeck College
University of London

ADDRESS FOR CORRESPONDENCE: Flat D
117 Waldegrave Road
Teddington
Middlesex
TW11 8LL

DURATION: 1986 - 1989

SOURCE OF FUNDING: Wingate Scholarship
The Harold Hyam Wingate Foundation
£7,492 (September to December 1989)

POLICE FORCES in which research carried out: Palestine Police

PROJECT SUMMARY:
To examine the breakdown of British civil and military control in Palestine in 1921, 1929 and 1936. Also to examine the extent to which the Mandate was policed, and how this was affected by ideological or other political beliefs.

METHODOLOGY:
Literature searches at the PRO in London, the Israeli State Archive in Jerusalem, Rhodes House, Oxford, RAF documentation at Hendon, and various personal and local archival sources.

PUBLICATIONS available or to be published:
-

PRINCIPAL INVESTIGATORS: LEN HARDY
GAYNOR PARFITT

TITLE OF PROJECT: THE RELATIONSHIP BETWEEN PHYSICAL FITNESS AND COPING WITH PSYCHOLOGICAL STRESS

Co WORKERS: Steven Baker

INSTITUTION: University College of North Wales

ADDRESS FOR CORRESPONDENCE: Physical Education Department
University College of North Wales
Bangor
Gwynedd
LL57 5DG

DURATION: February 1988 - April 1989

SOURCE OF FUNDING: Home Office PRSU £6,500
University College of North Wales £3,500

POLICE FORCES in which research carried out: Surrey Constabulary

PROJECT SUMMARY:
The project examines the relationship between different aspects of physical fitness and coping with psychological stress. Coping has been operationalised as short term coping and recovery from a specific job related stressor, together with more generalised mental well-being.

METHODOLOGY:
Multiple regression analysis is used to determine the relationship between aerobic, lactate system and ATP/PC fitness and several measures of mental well-being including proneness to stress related disease. An experimental protocol is being used to identify the influence of the physical fitness variables upon coping with communications stress in command control; coping is being measured by both biochemical and self report responses.

PUBLICATIONS available or to be published:
-

PRINCIPAL INVESTIGATOR: **CLEM HENRICSON**

TITLE OF PROJECT: **POLICE COMPLAINTS IN SOUTHWARK**

Co WORKERS: David Sanderson

INSTITUTION: Community Rights and Safety Policy Unit
Southwark Council

ADDRESS FOR CORRESPONDENCE: Community Rights and Safety Policy Unit
Southwark Council
Graca Machel House
207 Havil Street
London SE5

DURATION: January 1987 - January 1989

SOURCE OF FUNDING: Southwark Council
Metropolitan Police

POLICE FORCES in which research carried out: Metropolitan Police

PROJECT SUMMARY:
An analysis of the nature of police complaints in Southwark in relation to type of complaint, time, date, place, age, sex and ethnic origin. A comparison between the unregistered complaints data and the official complaints statistics. An analysis of the operation of the police complaints procedure.
Resulting from the research, a series of recommendations are made relating to training and management which are designed to reduce the number of complaints in the borough. A set of alterations to the complaints procedure are also recommended.

METHODOLOGY:
Interviews with the local area Police Complaints Unit, the Complaints Investigation Bureau, the Police Complaints Authority and the Police Federation.
Qualitative research undertaken in relation to the official complaints statistics for the period 1987 and the first 8 months of 1988.

PUBLICATIONS available or to be published:
Henricson C — Police Complaints in Southwark, Southwark Council, 1989.

PRINCIPAL INVESTIGATOR: BARNOR HESS

TITLE OF PROJECT: COUNCIL INQUIRY INTO RACIAL HARASSMENT

Co WORKERS: Dhanwant Rai
Massod Lone
Christine Bennett

INSTITUTION: London Borough of Waltham Forest

ADDRESS FOR CORRESPONDENCE: Police Unit
Room 223A
Waltham Forest Town Hall
Forest Road
London, E17 4JF

DURATION: November 1988 - November 1989

SOURCE OF FUNDING: London Borough of Waltham Forest £10,000

POLICE FORCES in which research carried out: Metropolitan Police

PROJECT SUMMARY:
To inquire into and comment on the extent, patterns and locations of racial harassment in Waltham Forest, with particular regard to the provision of Council services, the role and involvement of the police and the availability of support for victims of racial harassment.

METHODOLOGY:
Documentary research - analysis of Metropolitan Police reports, statistics, analysis of Council Committee Reports, statistics, previous research on racial harassment.

PUBLICATIONS available or to be published:
-

PRINCIPAL INVESTIGATOR: Dr MILES HEWSTONE

TITLE OF PROJECT: POLICE-SCHOOL LIAISON: AN EVALUATION

Co WORKERS: Dr Nicholas Hopkins

INSTITUTION: Bristol University

ADDRESS FOR CORRESPONDENCE: Department of Psychology
Bristol University
8-10 Berkeley Square
Bristol
BS8 HH1

DURATION: Summer 1987 - August 1989

SOURCE OF FUNDING: Home Office £36,000

POLICE FORCES in which research carried out: Avon and Somerset Constabulary

PROJECT SUMMARY:
Analysis of pupils' perceptions of the police, offending, school liaison officers, etc.

METHODOLOGY:
Questionnaire and interview survey of school pupils in a longitudinal study (test/re-test period of one year).

PUBLICATIONS available or to be published:
-

PRINCIPAL INVESTIGATOR: **MALCOLM HIBBERD**

TITLE OF PROJECT: **CRIME AND SMALL SHOPS**

Co WORKERS: Joanna Shapland

INSTITUTION: The Police Foundation

ADDRESS FOR CORRESPONDENCE: The Police Foundation
314/316 Vauxhall Bridge Road
London SW1V 1AA

DURATION: September 1987 - September 1989

SOURCE OF FUNDING: The Police Foundation £25,000

POLICE FORCES in which research carried out: Metropolitan Police, West Midlands Police

PROJECT SUMMARY:
A study of the victimisation of small retail outlets, with particular reference to the experiences of Asian retailers. The aim of the study will be to devise and develop preventative and defensive measures against victimisation.

METHODOLOGY:
Analysis of relevant records and interviews; survey of shop design and layout.

PUBLICATIONS available or to be published:
Hibberd M 'Violent crime and trouble in small shops', paper presented at the British Criminology conference, Bristol, July 1989

PRINCIPAL INVESTIGATOR: Dr DILYS HILL

TITLE OF PROJECT: THE NEW RIGHT AND INNER CITY

Co WORKERS: -

INSTITUTION: University of Southampton

ADDRESS FOR CORRESPONDENCE: Department of Politics
University of Southampton
Southampton
S09 5NH

DURATION: 1985 - June 1989

SOURCE OF FUNDING: -

POLICE FORCES in which research carried out: -

PROJECT SUMMARY:
To examine the changed agenda of the 1980's in relation to the problem of the inner cities in Great Britain and the United States.

METHODOLOGY:
Secondary analysis, interviews with policy makers.

PUBLICATIONS available or to be published:
-

PRINCIPAL INVESTIGATORS:	**GERARD HOGAN** **Dr CLIVE WALKER**
TITLE OF PROJECT:	**POLITICAL VIOLENCE AND THE LAW IN IRELAND**
Co WORKERS:	-
INSTITUTION:	Trinity College, Dublin University of Leeds
ADDRESS FOR CORRESPONDENCE:	Dr Clive Walker Centre for Criminal Justice Studies University of Leeds Leeds LS2 9JT
DURATION:	August 1986 - February 1989
SOURCE OF FUNDING:	-
POLICE FORCES in which research carried out:	Royal Ulster Constabulary Garda Siochana

PROJECT SUMMARY:
An account of the nature of political violence in Ireland, the principles on which legal measures against it should be based, a comprehensive survey of current legislation and case law, including extradition.

METHODOLOGY:
Examination of relevant law and practice, analysis of official documents and statistics.

PUBLICATIONS available or to be published:

Hogan G and Walker C	Political Violence and the Law in Ireland, Manchester University Press, 1989

PRINCIPAL INVESTIGATOR: Dr SIMON HOLDAWAY

TITLE OF PROJECT: ETHNIC MINORITY RECRUITMENT TO THE POLICE IN ENGLAND AND WALES

Co WORKERS: Fiona Quinn

INSTITUTION: University of Sheffield

ADDRESS FOR CORRESPONDENCE: Department of Sociology
University of Sheffield
Sheffield
S10 2TN

DURATION: January 1988 - June 1989

SOURCE OF FUNDING: Home Office £32,000

POLICE FORCES in which research carried out: National survey, three police forces for detailed research

PROJECT SUMMARY:
The research documents and analyses the range and content of British police initiatives to recruit and retain members of the ethnic minority groups.

METHODOLOGY
Formal questionnaires to every force in England and Wales requesting detailed information about policy and special initiatives in this area, as well as statistical data about related recruitment trends. Semi-structured interviews in three forces with ethnic minority officers about their experience of recruitment and in particular about their views on special initiatives.

PUBLICATIONS available or to be published:
-

PRINCIPAL INVESTIGATOR: SOHAIL HUSAIN

TITLE OF PROJECT: THE IMPACT OF NEIGHBOURHOOD WATCH ON HOUSEHOLD INSURANCE BURGLARY CLAIMS

Co WORKERS: -

INSTITUTION: Southampton University

ADDRESS FOR CORRESPONDENCE:
Urban Policy Research Unit
Department of Geography
The University
Southampton
S09 5NH

DURATION: January 1987 - June 1989

SOURCE OF FUNDING: Commercial Union Assurance Co

POLICE FORCES in which research carried out: Metropolitan Police, Bedfordshire Police, Cheshire Constabulary, Gloucestershire Constabulary, Kent Constabulary, Leicestershire Constabulary, Thames Valley Police, Warwickshire Constabulary, West Midlands Police

PROJECT SUMMARY:
Using data from insurance policies a comparison of the claims arising from burglary is made between areas in neighbourhood watch schemes and areas outside such schemes to assess their impact.

METHODOLOGY:
Policyholders have been contacted to ascertain their involvement in neighbourhood watch schemes. Areas have been classified according to insurance rating group and ACORN type to maximise control over residential environment.

PUBLICATIONS available or to be published:
-

PRINCIPAL INVESTIGATORS: LILLI HVINGTOFT-FOSTER
Dr ERIC SHEPHERD

TITLE OF PROJECT: THE POLICE PROBATIONARY PROCESS: CONSTRUING PERSONAL AND PROFESSIONAL CHANGE

Co WORKERS: -

INSTITUTION: City of London Polytechnic

ADDRESS FOR CORRESPONDENCE: Applied Psychology Unit
Department of Psychology
City of London Polytechnic
Old Castle Street
London, E1 7NT

DURATION: October 1988 - ongoing

SOURCE OF FUNDING: Rayne Trust

POLICE FORCES in which research carried out: Merseyside Police

PROJECT SUMMARY:
The aim is to map individual probationers' perceptions of their own personal and professional development as they proceed through the modular foundation programme.

METHODOLOGY:
Repertory grids, questionnaires and interviews at the beginning/end of each key module.

PUBLICATIONS available or to be published:
-

PRINCIPAL INVESTIGATOR: ANTHONY JACKSON

TITLE OF PROJECT: CONSTABULARY INDEPENDENCE AND ITS PLACE IN THE MODERN POLICE SERVICE: A LEGAL CRITIQUE

Co WORKERS: -

INSTITUTION: Polytechnic of Central London

ADDRESS FOR CORRESPONDENCE: 12 Lyons Drive
Worplesdon
Guildford
Surrey
GU2 6Y

DURATION: May 1984 - November 1988

SOURCE OF FUNDING: Unfunded

POLICE FORCES in which research carried out:

PROJECT SUMMARY:
The research challenges the traditional concept of constabulary independence and its existence in the modern police service. Comparisons are drawn throughout with employment relationships in public and private institutions and organisations. The original authority of a constable is assessed in key areas. These include the conditions of service which govern every person appointed as a police officer, existing disciplinary sanctions, and those powers and duties vested in them by the law itself. This is followed by a detailed critique of the legal responsibilities and powers of chief officers of police in their role as employers and their legal relationships with central government and local police authorities.

METHODOLOGY
Research has been based principally on authoritative detailed analysis of textbooks, law reports and legal commentaries. In addition the researcher has drawn on knowledge and first hand experience gained as a police officer.

PUBLICATIONS available or to be published:
-

PRINCIPAL INVESTIGATOR:	**GEORGINA JACKSON**
TITLE OF PROJECT:	**INDIVIDUAL DIFFERENCES IN THE ADJUSTMENT TO THE CONSTABLE/SERGEANT TRANSITION**
Co WORKERS:	Nigel Nicholson
INSTITUTION:	University of Sheffield
ADDRESS FOR CORRESPONDENCE:	MRC/ESRC Social & Applied Psychology Unit University of Sheffield Sheffield S10 2TN
DURATION:	October 1987 - September 1990
SOURCE OF FUNDING:	Economic and Social Research Council linked postgraduate award
POLICE FORCES in which research carried out:	Metropolitan Police

PROJECT SUMMARY:
The project focuses on adjustment to the rank of sergeant. In particular, the study investigates changes in role perception and role related knowledge (practical intelligence) across the transition from constable to sergeant. Individual differences in adjustment strategies, role perception, and work related judgements are also investigated.

METHODOLOGY:
A cohort of officers is being followed longitudinally across the transition from constable to sergeant. Data has been collected using questionnaires, supplemented by a small number of interviews. In addition, a small number of officers has taken part in a more focused investigation of practical intelligence. These measures have been supported by additional cross-sectional data.

PUBLICATIONS available or to be published:

Jackson, G — 'Expertise differences in the use of work related knowledge', paper presented at 4th West European Congress, Working with Change, Cambridge, April 1989

PRINCIPAL INVESTIGATOR: **AKRAM JASSIM**

TITLE OF PROJECT: **THE USE OF BROADCASTING MEDIA TO INVOLVE THE PUBLIC IN THE DETECTION AND PREVENTION OF CRIME**

Co WORKERS: -

INSTITUTION: Cranfield Institute of Technology

ADDRESS FOR CORRESPONDENCE: Department of Social Policy
Cranfield Institute of Technology
Cranfield
Bedford
MK43 0AL

DURATION: - July 1989

SOURCE OF FUNDING: Postgraduate funding

POLICE FORCES in which research carried out: -

PROJECT SUMMARY:
To discuss and evaluate the use of broadcasting media, television and radio, by the police to elicit public involvement in solving and preventing crime in the UK.

METHODOLOGY:
Content analysis of numbers of current television programmes such as Crimewatch UK, Police 5 London, Police 5 South.
Mail survey to all public relations officers in all police forces to find out their opinion on these programmes and on the use of broadcasting media in general.
Interviews with key persons in the police service and the media.

PUBLICATIONS available or to be published:
-

PRINCIPAL INVESTIGATORS:	**TONY JEFFERSON** **MONICA A WALKER**
TITLE OF PROJECT:	**ETHNIC MINORITIES, YOUNG PEOPLE AND THE CRIMINAL JUSTICE SYSTEM**
Co WORKERS:	M Seneviratne H Szulc
INSTITUTION:	Sheffield University
ADDRESS FOR CORRESPONDENCE:	Centre for Criminological and Socio-Legal Studies Sheffield University 430-432 Crookesmoor Road Sheffield S10 1BL
DURATION:	April 1986 - April 1989
SOURCE OF FUNDING:	Economic and Social Research Council £73,850
POLICE FORCES in which research carried out:	West Yorkshire Police

PROJECT SUMMARY:
Comparisons are made between the proportions of males aged 10-35 who are arrested from the Afro-Caribbean, Asian and white populations. A survey in the community compares their attitudes to and experiences of the police. Court observation investigates treatment by the courts and prosecution and court statistics are analysed.

METHODOLOGY:
1. Recording of the details of all males aged 10-35 arrested or stopped in 6 sub-divisions of Leeds from 1 June 1987 for six months. Analysis by race, offence and area of residence, to investigate relative rates for Afro-Caribbean, Asian and white offenders.
2. Survey of 200 Afro-Caribbean, 200 Asian and 200 white residents to examine experiences and attitudes to the police. This will be carried out by a market research company.

PUBLICATIONS available or to be published:

Walker M A	'The ethnic origin of prisons', British Journal of Criminology, 27, 1987, 202-6
Walker M A	'Interpreting race and crime statistics', J. Roy. Statist. Soc., 150, 1987, 39-56

PRINCIPAL INVESTIGATOR: LES JOHNSTON

TITLE OF PROJECT: PRIVATISATION AND THE 'NEW POLICING'

Co WORKERS: -

INSTITUTION: University of Exeter

ADDRESS FOR CORRESPONDENCE:
Centre for Police Studies
University of Exeter
Brookfield Annexe
New North Road
Exeter, EX4 4JY

DURATION: January 1989 - January 1991

SOURCE OF FUNDING: Unfunded

POLICE FORCES in which research carried out: -

PROJECT SUMMARY:
An examination of the expansion and role of private security in Britain and Europe, looking at quasi-private police forces, active citizenship and private policing initiatives, and public and private dimensions of social control.

METHODOLOGY:
Secondary sources including trade literature from West Europe, interviews with police policy-makers, interviews with industry.

PUBLICATIONS available or to be published:

Johnston L — 'Privatisation and the police function', in Reiner R and Cross M (eds) Beyond Law and Order, Macmillan, 1990.

PRINCIPAL INVESTIGATOR: PATRICIA JONES

TITLE OF PROJECT: DETENTION UNDER THE POLICE AND CRIMINAL EVIDENCE ACT 1984

Co WORKERS: -

INSTITUTION: University College of Wales, Aberystwyth

ADDRESS FOR CORRESPONDENCE:
Law Department
University College of Wales, Aberystwyth
Penglais Hill
Aberystwyth
Dyfed, SY23 2AX

DURATION: October 1988 - September 1990

SOURCE OF FUNDING: Unfunded

POLICE FORCES in which research carried out:
Dyfed Powys Police
South Wales Constabulary

PROJECT SUMMARY:
Examination of the right of silence, and the effect of the Police and Criminal Evidence Act on police work.

PUBLICATIONS available or to be published:
-

PRINCIPAL INVESTIGATOR:	**LIZ KELLY**
TITLE OF PROJECT:	**THE PREVALENCE OF CHILD SEXUAL ABUSE IN BRITAIN**
Co WORKERS:	-
INSTITUTION:	Polytechnic of North London
ADDRESS FOR CORRESPONDENCE:	Child Abuse Studies Unit School of Health and Social Work Polytechnic of North London Ladbroke House 62-66 Highbury Grove London, N5 2AD
DURATION:	April 1989 - January 1991
SOURCE OF FUNDING:	Economic and Social Research Council £70,000
POLICE FORCES in which research carried out:	-

PROJECT SUMMARY:
To assess the prevalence of child sexual abuse in a national sample of 1,200 young people (16-21)

METHODOLOGY
Self-report questionnaires.

PUBLICATIONS available or to be published:
-

PRINCIPAL INVESTIGATOR:	**JOHN KNOWLES**
TITLE OF PROJECT:	**THE EFFECTIVENESS AND EFFICIENCY OF A DEDICATED TRAINING RELIEF**
Co WORKERS:	Dr Steve Stradling Dr Mike Chatterton
INSTITUTION:	Manchester University
ADDRESS FOR CORRESPONDENCE:	Personnel Services Lancashire Constabulary Hutton Preston PR4 5SB
DURATION:	October 1988 - September 1989
SOURCE OF FUNDING:	Bramshill Fellowship
POLICE FORCES in which research carried out:	Lancashire Constabulary

PROJECT SUMMARY:
The establishment of an independent, dedicated training scale based in a territorial division. Observation of that training scale together with training arrangements in two adjacent divisions over four intakes of probationers, covering a seven month period.

METHODOLOGY:
Task/experience recording, questionnaire, participant observation and in-depth interviews of both tutors and probationers.

PUBLICATIONS available or to be published:
-

PRINCIPAL INVESTIGATOR: ROD LEEMING

TITLE OF PROJECT: AN ASSESSMENT OF THE COSTS OF VIP PROTECTION

Co WORKERS: -

INSTITUTION: University of Exeter

ADDRESS FOR CORRESPONDENCE:
Centre for Police Studies
University of Exeter
Brookfield Annexe
New North Road
Exeter, EX4 4JY

DURATION: October 1988 - October 1989

SOURCE OF FUNDING: Bramshill Fellowship

POLICE FORCES in which research carried out: -

PROJECT SUMMARY:
An investigation of the costs of the present system of VIP protection and alternative systems. Scrutiny of criteria of appropriateness related to level of threat.

METHODOLOGY:
Cost-benefit analysis.

PUBLICATIONS available or to be published:
-

PRINCIPAL INVESTIGATOR: M S LEES

TITLE OF PROJECT: DETENTION IN THE UNITED KINGDOM

Co WORKERS: -

INSTITUTION: University of Hull

ADDRESS FOR CORRESPONDENCE: The Faculty of Law
University of Hull
Hull
HU6 7RX

DURATION: 1984 -

SOURCE OF FUNDING: -

POLICE FORCES in which research carried out: -

PROJECT SUMMARY:
An analysis of the justification for, and aims of detention of certain categories of people within the United Kingdom, including prisoners, mentally ill offenders, detainees under the Police and Criminal Evidence Act 1984, and political detainees in Northern Ireland.

PUBLICATIONS available or to be published:

Lees M — 'Changing the national rules: the ECHR and the detention of prisoners and mentally ill offenders', in Yearbook of Social Policy, Longman, 1987, 198-221

PRINCIPAL INVESTIGATOR: Dr MICHAEL LEVI

TITLE OF PROJECT: POLICE-BANK CONFIDENTIALITY AND COOPERATION

Co WORKERS: -

INSTITUTION: University of Wales, College of Cardiff

ADDRESS FOR CORRESPONDENCE: School of Social and Administrative Studies
University of Wales, College of Cardiff
62 Cardiff Place
Cardiff
CF1 3AS

DURATION: March 1988 - July 1989

SOURCE OF FUNDING: Police Foundation £2,000

POLICE FORCES in which research carried out: A number of forces and banks nationwide

PROJECT SUMMARY:
The project examines the development of the powers of the police to require information from banking institutions, and the obligations of bankers to inform the police proactively (eg drugs, terrorism) of 'suspicious' transactions. It looks at how these powers are exercised in practice, nationally and internationally, and what are the obstacles to better communication between policing agencies and the banks, as well as how effective in attaining police objectives demands on the banks are likely to be.

METHODOLOGY:
Interviews and documentary evidence.

PUBLICATIONS available or to be published:
Report to be published shortly.

PRINCIPAL INVESTIGATOR:	**Dr MICHAEL LEVI**
TITLE OF PROJECT:	**A SURVEY OF SENIOR EXECUTIVES' ATTITUDES TO FRAUD AND ITS REGULATION**
Co WORKERS:	James Morgan
INSTITUTION:	University of Wales, College of Cardiff
ADDRESS FOR CORRESPONDENCE:	School of Social & Administrative Studies University of Wales, College of Cardiff 62 Park Place Cardiff CF1 3AS
DURATION:	June 1989 - January 1990
SOURCE OF FUNDING:	Ernst and Young
POLICE FORCES in which research carried out:	-

PROJECT SUMMARY:
The project examines the extent and nature of fraud against large corporations and executives' attitudes towards its regulation, including their satisfaction with and expectations of policing agencies involved.

METHODOLOGY:
Survey questionnaire and interviews.

PUBLICATIONS available or to be published:
A report will be published.

Levi M	Regulating Fraud, Tavistock/Routledge, 1987
Levi M	The Prevention of Fraud, Home Office Crime Prevention Unit Paper 17, 1988

PRINCIPAL INVESTIGATOR:	**KEN LIDSTONE**
TITLE OF PROJECT:	**SEARCH AND SEIZURE: AN EVALUATION OF PART II OF THE POLICE AND CRIMINAL EVIDENCE ACT 1984**
Co WORKERS:	Vaughan Bevan Vanessa Saxton
INSTITUTION:	University of Sheffield
ADDRESS FOR CORRESPONDENCE:	Centre for Criminological and Socio-Legal Studies University of Sheffield 430-432 Crookesmoor Road Sheffield, S10 1BL
DURATION:	September 1987 - February 1990
SOURCE OF FUNDING:	Economic and Social Research Council £50,570
POLICE FORCES in which research carried out:	-

PROJECT SUMMARY:
The study examines the use made by the police of the powers to enter and search premises and to seize property provided by Part II of the Police and Criminal Evidence Act 1984 and other statutory powers of search and seeks to assess the effectiveness of these powers in the investigation of crime and the effectiveness of safeguards against abuse of these powers provided by the 1984 Act.

METHODOLOGY:
Search registers form the basis for the collection of data. A sample of police officers authorising and exercising the powers will be interviewed, as will a sample of the householders or occupiers of the premises searched. In addition a member of the research team will accompany the police on some of the searches and spend time with some of the squads, such as the Drug Squad, in order to see the search operations at first hand.

PUBLICATIONS available or to be published:
-

PRINCIPAL INVESTIGATOR: **JOHN LIGGETT**

TITLE OF PROJECT: **A NEW METHOD FOR ASSISTING RECALL OF FACES BY WITNESSES**

Co WORKERS: -

INSTITUTION: University of Wales, College of Cardiff

ADDRESS FOR CORRESPONDENCE: PLWCCA Lodge
Pendoylan
Cowbridge
South Glamorgan, CF7 7UL

DURATION: 1986 - 1989

SOURCE OF FUNDING: Nuffield Foundation

POLICE FORCES in which research carried out: South Wales Constabulary

PROJECT SUMMARY:
A small, inexpensive and portable 'facial synthesis' has now been perfected, tested and patented which enables witnesses to create a realistic image of a criminal when the equipment is connected to a domestic television set aerial socket.

METHODOLOGY:
Current work is concerned with refinement of the relatively small number of photographs of facial parts which are coalesced in the equipment. Work is in progress on an ethnic and a female series of parts.

PUBLICATIONS available or to be published:
Description and report available from investigator.

PRINCIPAL INVESTIGATOR: BARRY LOVEDAY

TITLE OF PROJECT: GOVERNMENT OF THE METROPOLITAN AREAS SINCE ABOLITION OF METROPOLITAN POLICE AUTHORITIES

Co WORKERS: Steve Leach

INSTITUTION: Birmingham University (INLOGOV) and Birmingham Polytechnic

ADDRESS FOR CORRESPONDENCE:
Department of Government and Economics
Birmingham Polytechnic
Perry Barr
Birmingham
B42 2SU

DURATION: September 1987 - April 1989

SOURCE OF FUNDING: INLOGOV, University of Birmingham £8,500

POLICE FORCES in which research carried out: Metropolitan police authorities

PROJECT SUMMARY:
The research considers the operation of the Joint Boards for police in the Metropolitan areas from 1985/86 to date. Data collected on district members, magistrates, officer-member relations, policy development, impact on tripartite relationship, ratecapping and permitted expenditure levels, manpower and civilianisation.

METHODOLOGY:
The research has been conducted primarily by use of interviews with police authority officers and members, Home Office officials, use of official documents and committee minutes.

PUBLICATIONS available or to be published:

Loveday B — 'Joint Boards for police in the Metropolitan areas: A preliminary assessment', Local Government Studies, May/June 1987.

Loveday B — 'The Joint Boards', Policing, Vol 3, Autumn 1987

Loveday B — Joint Boards and the local accountability of police in the Metropolitan areas 1988, paper for the Research Steering Committee, INLOGOV, Birmingham University (available from Birmingham Polytechnic)

PRINCIPAL INVESTIGATORS:	**Dr MIKE McCONVILLE** **ROGER LENG** **ANDREW SANDERS**
TITLE OF PROJECT:	**DISCRETION TO CHARGE AND TO PROSECUTE**
Co WORKERS:	Vanessa Saxton (to Dec '87) Robert Wight
INSTITUTION:	University of Birmingham University of Warwick
ADDRESS FOR CORRESPONDENCE:	Andrew Sanders Faculty of Law University of Birmingham Birmingham B15 2TT and Mike McConville School of Law University of Warwick Coventry CV4 7AL
DURATION:	January 1986 - March 1989
SOURCE OF FUNDING:	Economic and Social Research Council £53,430
POLICE FORCES in which research carried out:	3 police forces

PROJECT SUMMARY:
To examine the discretion to charge and to prosecute. In particular to study cautioning, case construction, the inter-relationship between the police and the prosecution service and case vetting.

METHODOLOGY:
1,080 cases were collected in two police stations in each of three police forces. The cases were monitored from arrest or report until final disposal. All relevant decision makers in the police and the Crown Prosecution Service were interviewed about each of the cases.

PUBLICATIONS available or to be published:
-

PRINCIPAL INVESTIGATORS:	**Dr MIKE McCONVILLE** **DAN SHEPHERD**
TITLE OF PROJECT:	**NEIGHBOURHOOD WATCH AND COMMUNITY POLICING**
Co WORKERS:	-
INSTITUTION:	University of Warwick
ADDRESS FOR CORRESPONDENCE:	Legal Research Institute School of Law University of Warwick Coventry CV4 7AL
DURATION:	October 1988 - September 1990
SOURCE OF FUNDING:	Barrow and Geraldine S. Cadbury Trust
POLICE FORCES in which research carried out:	3 police forces

PROJECT SUMMARY AND METHODOLOGY:
Observational work with home beat officers.
Structured interviews with watch officers and non-watch officers.

PUBLICATIONS available or to be published:
-

PRINCIPAL INVESTIGATORS:	**Det Sgt ANDREW McDIARMID** **Dr ERIC SHEPHERD**
TITLE OF PROJECT:	**DEVELOPING ECOLOGICALLY VALID MEASURES OF INTERROGATIVE SUGGESTIBILITY**
Co WORKERS:	-
INSTITUTION:	City of London Polytechnic Merseyside Police Interview Development Unit
ADDRESS FOR CORRESPONDENCE:	Centre for Interview Research and Development Department of Psychology City of London Polytechnic Old Castle Street London, E1 7NT
DURATION:	February 1988 - ongoing
SOURCE OF FUNDING:	Unfunded
POLICE FORCES in which research carried out:	Merseyside Police

PROJECT SUMMARY:
The aim is to examine empirically factors which could contribute to and detract from the development of a measure of interviewee suggestibility.

METHODOLOGY:
A five stage programme of empirical experimentation.

PUBLICATIONS available or to be published:

Shepherd E and McDiarmid A	'Shaping questions: shaping answers', (forthcoming article)

PRINCIPAL INVESTIGATORS:	**ALISON McGIBBON** **LIBBY COOPER** **LIZ KELLY**
TITLE OF PROJECT:	**WHAT SUPPORT? HAMMERSMITH AND FULHAM COUNCIL COMMUNITY POLICE COMMITTEE DOMESTIC VIOLENCE PROJECT**
Co WORKERS:	-
INSTITUTION:	Polytechnic of North London
ADDRESS FOR CORRESPONDENCE:	Ladbroke House Highbury Grove London N5 2AD
DURATION:	June 1988 - February 1989
SOURCE OF FUNDING:	Hammersmith and Fulham Council £15,000
POLICE FORCES in which research carried out:	Metropolitan Police

PROJECT SUMMARY:
To investigate the service available in Hammersmith and Fulham for women who have experienced or are experiencing domestic violence. The study focuses on women's experiences, the responses of statutory and voluntary agencies to domestic violence and includes recommendations for changes in policy and practice and for development of services.

METHODOLOGY:
Action research based.
Questionnaire surveys, in-depth interviews.

PUBLICATIONS available or to be published:

McGibbon A, Cooper L and Kelly L	What Support ?, Hammersmith and Fulham Council Community Police Committee Domestic Violence Project, final report, March 1989

PRINCIPAL INVESTIGATOR: NORRIE MACKILLOP

TITLE OF PROJECT: POLICING CRIME IN THE CHINESE COMMUNITY IN THE UK

Co WORKERS: -

INSTITUTION: University of Exeter

ADDRESS FOR CORRESPONDENCE: Centre for Police Studies
University of Exeter
Brookfield Annexe
New North Road
Exeter, EX4 4JY

DURATION: October 1988 - October 1989

SOURCE OF FUNDING: Postgraduate funding

POLICE FORCES in which research carried out: Metropolitan Police, West Midlands Police, Greater Manchester Police

PROJECT SUMMARY:
Examination of origin of the UK Chinese community, its structure and social organisation. Investigation of the effects of these on the nature of crime in the community and the police response. The mythology of the importance of triads is also discussed.

METHODOLOGY:
Interviews and comparison with Hong Kong.

PUBLICATIONS available or to be published:
A Brookfield Paper will be published in January 1990.

PRINCIPAL INVESTIGATOR:	**JOHN MACLEOD**
TITLE OF PROJECT:	**ETHNIC MINORITIES AND THE CRIMINAL JUSTICE SYSTEM**
Co WORKERS:	-
INSTITUTION:	Research and Planning Unit, Home Office
ADDRESS FOR CORRESPONDENCE:	Research and Planning Unit Home Office 50 Queen Anne's Gate London SW1H 9AT
DURATION:	6 months
SOURCE OF FUNDING:	Home Office
POLICE FORCES in which research carried out:	Metropolitan Police, Leicestershire Constabulary

PROJECT SUMMARY:
A statistical analysis of the tape recording data of the experience of ethnic minorities in the criminal justice system with special attention to bail/remand and sentencing patterns.

METHODOLOGY:
Multi-dimensional contingency table analysis using log-linear modelling techniques to identify the factors influencing the various divisions in the criminal justice process.

PUBLICATIONS available or to be published:
-

PRINCIPAL INVESTIGATOR: JOHN MACLEOD

TITLE OF PROJECT: STUDIES OF TAPE-RECORDING

Co WORKERS: -

INSTITUTION: Research and Planning Unit, Home Office

ADDRESS FOR CORRESPONDENCE: Research and Planning Unit
Home Office
50 Queen Anne's Gate
London
SW1H 9AT

DURATION: - Summer 1990

SOURCE OF FUNDING: Home Office

POLICE FORCES in which research carried out: Merseyside Police, Leicester Constabulary, Northumbria Police, Hampshire Constabulary, Metropolitan Police

PROJECT SUMMARY:
Field trials of the tape-recording of police interviews with suspects have been monitored in several forces. This project assesses the extent to which the predicted benefits of tape recording have been realsied. A follow up study to evaluate the long term effects of tape-recording is in the planning stage.

METHODOLOGY:
A longitudinal data collection following suspects through from arrest to disposal in court or earlier release.

PUBLICATIONS available or to be published:

Willis C — The tape-recording of police interviews with suspects: an interim report, Home Office Research Study No 82, HMSO, 1984

Willis C, Macleod J and Naish J — The tape-recording of police interviews with suspects: a second interim report, Home Office Research Study No 97, HMSO, 1988

PRINCIPAL INVESTIGATOR:	**EWAN MACPHERSON**
TITLE OF PROJECT:	**A REVIEW OF THE EFFECTIVENESS OF POLICE CONSULTATIVE COMMITTEES**
Co WORKERS:	-
INSTITUTION:	University of Exeter
ADDRESS FOR CORRESPONDENCE:	Centre for Police Studies University of Exeter Brookfield Annexe New North Road Exeter, EX4 4JY
DURATION:	October 1989 - October 1990
SOURCE OF FUNDING:	Postgraduate funding
POLICE FORCES in which research carried out:	Metropolitan Police

PROJECT SUMMARY:
Comparison of five police community consultative committees.

METHODOLOGY:
Document survey and interviews.

PUBLICATIONS available or to be published:
-

PRINCIPAL INVESTIGATOR:	**MIKE MAGUIRE**
TITLE OF PROJECT:	**COMPLAINTS AGAINST THE POLICE**
Co WORKERS:	Claire Corbett (Brunel University)
INSTITUTION:	University of Wales, College of Cardiff
ADDRESS FOR CORRESPONDENCE:	School of Social and Administrative Studies University of Wales, College of Cardiff 62 Park Place Cardiff CF1 3AS
DURATION:	October 1986 - December 1988
SOURCE OF FUNDING:	Home Office £126,000
POLICE FORCES in which research carried out:	3 police forces

PROJECT SUMMARY:
Analysis, evaluation and discussion of the work of the Police Complaints Authority, patterns and profiles of complaints, the investigation process, withdrawn and informally resolved complaints and views of police officers, complainants and investigators.

METHODOLOGY:
Complaints file analysis, interviews, postal survey, observation.

PUBLICATIONS available or to be published:

Maguire M and Corbett C	'Patterns and profiles of complaints against the police', in Morgan R and Smith D (eds) <u>Coming to Terms with Policing</u>, Routledge, 1989
Maguire M	'Complaints against the police in England and Wales' in Goldsmith A (ed) <u>Police Complaints Proceedings in Seven Countries</u>, Oxford University Press, 1990

A book is planned.

PRINCIPAL INVESTIGATORS:	**MIKE MAGUIRE** **Dr DICK HOBBS**
TITLE OF PROJECT:	**THE NATURE OF DETECTIVE WORK AND THE EVALUATION OF POLICE INVESTIGATIVE PERFORMANCE**
Co WORKERS:	Nigel Brearley Lesley Noaks
INSTITUTION:	University of Wales, College of Cardiff Polytechnic of Central London
ADDRESS FOR CORRESPONDENCE:	School of Social and Administrative Studies University of Wales, College of Cardiff 62 Park Place Cardiff CF1 3AS
DURATION:	April 1989 - March 1991
SOURCE OF FUNDING:	Home Office £114,972
POLICE FORCES in which research carried out:	To be decided

PROJECT SUMMARY:
To evaluate various alternatives to the clear-up rate as measures of police investigative performance. This will be carried out in the context of a study of police (and particularly CID) culture and working practices. The researchers will also look at the presentation of investigative performance in the media.

METHODOLOGY:
Crime file analysis, interviews, observational research.

PUBLICATIONS available or to be published:
-

PRINCIPAL INVESTIGATOR: **ANNE MANDEVILLE**

TITLE OF PROJECT: **THE MAINTENANCE OF LAW AND ORDER IN THE UNITED KINGDOM**

Co WORKERS: -

INSTITUTION: Institut d'Etudes Poliques de l'Universite de Toulouse
Centre d'Etudes et de Recherches sur l'Armee
Centre for Defence and Security Analysis, Lancaster University

ADDRESS FOR CORRESPONDENCE: Institut d'Etudes Poliques de l'Universite de Toulouse
5 Impasse de la Colombette
31 000 Toulouse
France

DURATION: 1984 - 1989/90

SOURCE OF FUNDING: 3 year fellowship from the Centre National de la Recherche Scientifique (France) and Economic and Social Research Council

POLICE FORCES in which research carried out: -

PROJECT SUMMARY:
The project examines the maintenance of public order in the UK, particularly the concept of the Queen's Peace and its perception and practice by the security forces in the United Kingdom. The project also provides a comparative analysis of the system of maintenance of order in France and in the United Kingdom.

METHODOLOGY:
Study of legal material, a review of the British press on the subject (from the year 1982), a selective study of press and reviews on a historic basis, a literature search of research material, police and military publications, interviews with members of the security forces, civil servants and visits to military and police institutions.

PUBLICATIONS available or to be published:

Mandeville A — 'The British army in Northern Ireland: new professionalism', in Edmonds M (ed) British Military Systems, Brassey's, 1986.

PRINCIPAL INVESTIGATOR: PETER MANNING

TITLE OF PROJECT: POLICE RESPONSES TO 999/911 CALLS

Co WORKERS: -

INSTITUTION: Michigan State University or Socio-Legal Centre, Oxford University

ADDRESS FOR CORRESPONDENCE: Department of Sociology
Michigan State University
E Lansing
MI 48824
USA

DURATION: November 1979 - ongoing

SOURCE OF FUNDING: Unfunded

POLICE FORCES in which research carried out: West Midlands Police
Metropolitan Police
Detroit (USA)

PROJECT SUMMARY:
An analysis of the semiotics of communication in organisational contexts based on fieldwork in Detroit, Michigan and the West Midlands Police communications centres.

METHODOLOGY:
Interviews with a small number of officers to give a background view rather than statistical data.

PUBLICATIONS available or to be published:

Manning P	The Drama of Police: A theory, University of Chicago Press (forthcoming)
Manning P and Hawkins K	'Police decision-making' in Weatheritt M (ed) Police Research: some future prospects, Gower, 1989

PRINCIPAL INVESTIGATOR: PERCY MATHER

TITLE OF PROJECT: THE PERMANENT BEAT OFFICER SYSTEM - MEASURING ITS EFFICIENCY AND EFFECTIVENESS

Co WORKERS: -

INSTITUTION: University of Newcastle upon Tyne

ADDRESS FOR CORRESPONDENCE: Northumbria Police Force Headquarters
Ponteland
Newcastle upon Tyne
NE20 OBL

DURATION: September 1988 - September 1989

SOURCE OF FUNDING: Northumbria Police Authority following award of Bramshill Fellowship

POLICE FORCES in which research carried out: Northumbria Police
Derbyshire Constabulary
States of Jersey Police
Surrey Constabulary

PROJECT SUMMARY:
The aim of the research is to establish what, if any, benefits are derived from a community policing strategy known in the host force as permanent beat officer policing, how the role and function of those officers is perceived by colleagues, supervisors and the public and whether the latter generally perceive themselves to be more appropriately policed where a P.B.O. system operates.

METHODOLOGY:
Questionnaires to police officers concerning the role and function of permanent beat officers, and to members of the public concerning their perceptions of criminality in the area in which they live and the police response to it. Follow up interviews of selected respondents which focus on specific items of importance. Secondary research by correspondence and possible visits to other forces to assess the impact of their community policing strategies. The foregoing to be supplemented by literature research.

PUBLICATIONS available or to be published:
-

PRINCIPAL INVESTIGATOR: PERCY MATHER

TITLE OF PROJECT: THE PROBLEM SOLVING APPROACH FOR POLICE TRAINING - A STRATEGY FOR TEACHING AND LEARNING

Co WORKERS: -

INSTITUTION: Newcastle upon Tyne Polytechnic

ADDRESS FOR CORRESPONDENCE: Northumbria Police
Force Headquarters
Ponteland
Newcastle upon Tyne
NE20 0BL

DURATION: January 1985 - November 1987

SOURCE OF FUNDING: Unfunded

POLICE FORCES in which research carried out: Northumbria Police

PROJECT SUMMARY:
The aim of the project is to establish what attitudinal changes, positive or negative, occur as the result of the initial training course for police recruits. In addition, teaching strategies are assessed and learning styles identified to establish the best recruit teaching environment.

METHODOLOGY:
Recruits completed questionnaires prior to attending district training centres. On return from the course, recruits again completed questionnaires and any shift in attitudes was noted. Separately, students attending progress and monitoring courses completed course perception questionnaires commenting upon efficacy of classroom environment. 147 students completed attitudinal questionnaires. 222 students completed course perceptions questionnaires.

PUBLICATIONS available or to be published:
-

PRINCIPAL INVESTIGATORS: Dr ROB MAWBY
MARTIN GILL

TITLE OF PROJECT: VOLUNTEERS IN THE CRIMINAL JUSTICE SYSTEM: A COMPARATIVE ANALYSIS: POLICE SPECIALS

Co WORKERS: -

INSTITUTION: Polytechnic of the South West

ADDRESS FOR CORRESPONDENCE: Department of Social and Political Studies
Polytechnic of the South West
15 Portland Villas
Plymouth

DURATION: September 1983 - August 1989

SOURCE OF FUNDING: Polytechnic Research Assistantship

POLICE FORCES in which research carried out: Devon and Cornwall Constabulary, but wider project includes national and international material.

PROJECT SUMMARY:
An analysis of the role of police volunteers, historically and cross-nationally. Alternative models of public involvement. Focus on police specials in England and Wales and particularly in Devon and Cornwall, with detailed material on police officers' perspectives of specials and specials' work and motivation, and the development of a volunteer subculture. Comparison with probation and victim services.

METHODOLOGY:
Informal discussions, participant observation, analysis of official records, questionnaires (postal and personal interviews). Parallel methodology vis a vis probation and victim support volunteers.

PUBLICATIONS available or to be published:

Gill M — 'The Special Constabulary: community representation and the accountability question', in Mawby R I (ed) Policing Britain: Current Issues, Plymouth Polytechnic, 1987

Gill M and Mawby R I — Volunteers and the Criminal Justice System, Open University Press, 1989

PRINCIPAL INVESTIGATOR: Dr ROB MAWBY

TITLE OF PROJECT: COMPARATIVE POLICING ISSUES

Co WORKERS: -

INSTITUTION: Polytechnic of the South West

ADDRESS FOR CORRESPONDENCE: Department of Social and Political Studies
Polytechnic of the South West
15 Portland Villas
Plymouth

DURATION: September 1987 - December 1989

SOURCE OF FUNDING: -

POLICE FORCES in which research carried out: -

PROJECT SUMMARY:
This project involves a detailed analysis of policing systems, their development and current operations, in a number of countries. The project focuses on selected countries including France, Netherlands, Japan, China and Cuba, and special issues viewed cross-culturally (including community involvement and firearms).

METHODOLOGY:
Secondary analysis and literature review.

PUBLICATIONS available or to be published:

Mawby R I — Comparative Policing Issues, Unwin Hyman, 1990

PRINCIPAL INVESTIGATOR: Dr ROB MAWBY

TITLE OF PROJECT: NEIGHBOURHOOD WATCH IN RURAL AREAS

Co WORKERS: -

INSTITUTION: Polytechnic of the South West

ADDRESS FOR CORRESPONDENCE: Department of Social and Political Studies
Polytechnic of the South West
15 Portland Villas
Plymouth

DURATION: October 1988 - August 1990

SOURCE OF FUNDING: -

POLICE FORCES in which research carried out: Devon and Cornwall Constabulary

PROJECT SUMMARY:
Analysis of the development of neighbourhood watch schemes in the South West, with particular emphasis on who becomes involved and why.

METHODOLOGY:
Informal discussions with policy-makers.
Official records.
Questionnaire for scheme coordinators.

PUBLICATIONS available or to be published:
-

PRINCIPAL INVESTIGATORS: Sgt JONATHAN MEREDITH
Dr ERIC SHEPHERD

TITLE OF PROJECT: COPING WITH THE INTERVIEWEE: THE RELATIONSHIP BETWEEN INTERVIEWERS' PERSON PERCEPTION AND THEIR INTERVIEWING BEHAVIOUR

Co WORKERS: -

INSTITUTION: City of London Polytechnic

ADDRESS FOR CORRESPONDENCE: Centre for Interview Research and Development
Department of Psychology
City of London Polytechnic
Old Castle Street
London, E1 7NT

DURATION: October 1988 -

SOURCE OF FUNDING: Unfunded

POLICE FORCES in which research carried out: City of London Police

PROJECT SUMMARY:
Applying 'quadrant behaviour analysis' and standard measures of person perception to establish the links between interviewers' perceptions of interviewees and the interviewers' management of the subsequent interview.

METHODOLOGY:
Detailed content analysis of interviews (PACE tape recordings), interviews of and questionnaires to interviewers involved.

PUBLICATIONS available or to be published:
-

PRINCIPAL INVESTIGATOR: BONNY MHLANGA

TITLE OF PROJECT: CRIMINAL JUSTICE AND ETHNIC MINORITIES IN BRENT

Co WORKERS: Dr Nigel Fielding
Dr Jane Fielding

INSTITUTION: University of Surrey

ADDRESS FOR CORRESPONDENCE: Department of Sociology
University of Surrey
Guildford
Surrey
GU2 5XH

DURATION: October 1984 - October 1989

SOURCE OF FUNDING: Unfunded

POLICE FORCES in which research carried out: Metropolitan Police

PROJECT SUMMARY:
The project seeks to delineate factors which impact on outcomes in the institutional processing of young offenders on a cross-cultural basis; to test a differential outcome hypothesis between young defendants of different races following the Criminal Justice Act 1982 and to compare local with regional (London area) and national trends.

METHODOLOGY:
Quantitative data analysis from police and inter-departmental records of the flow of referrals and outcomes in the local juvenile criminal justice system, in the period up to 5 years from the inception of the Criminal Justice Act 1982.
Participant observation of the system as a full-time local authority social worker.

PUBLICATIONS available or to be published:
-

PRINCIPAL INVESTIGATOR:	**MARGARET MITCHELL**
TITLE OF PROJECT:	**PREDICTION OF POLICE OFFICERS' RECOVERY FROM INJURY**
Co WORKERS:	Professor Keith Oatley
INSTITUTION:	University of Glasgow
ADDRESS FOR CORRESPONDENCE:	Department of Psychology University of Glasgow Adam Smith Building Glasgow, G12 8RT
DURATION:	1988-1989
SOURCE OF FUNDING:	Scottish Police Federation Police Foundation Police Surgeons Association of Great Britain
POLICE FORCES in which research carried out:	Strathclyde Police

PROJECT SUMMARY:
An investigation of physical and psychological factors which ten to predict recovery from common moderate injuries in the police.

PUBLICATIONS available or to be published:

Mitchell M, McLay W and Oatley K — 'The affective state of officers convalescing after accidental injury both on and off duty', The Police Surgeon, No 34, November 1988.

PRINCIPAL INVESTIGATOR: TONY MOORE

TITLE OF PROJECT: PRINCIPLES OF POLICING PUBLIC DISORDER

Co WORKERS: -

INSTITUTION: University of Southampton

ADDRESS FOR CORRESPONDENCE: Nursery Cottage
Crondall Road
Crookham Village
Aldershot
GU13 0SY

DURATION: January 1987 - December 1990

SOURCE OF FUNDING: Unfunded

POLICE FORCES in which research carried out: -

PROJECT SUMMARY:
The aim of the research is two-fold. Firstly, it is intended to develop the concepts of 'Grand Strategy' and 'Strategy' for the policing of public disorder. Secondly, it aims to develop a set of principles for policing public disorder.

METHODOLOGY:
Researching into selected outbreaks of serious public disorder occurring between 1829 and 1986.
Interviewing senior police officers who have been involved in the policing of serious public disorder or who are regarded as experts in this particular field.
Interviewing academics who are regarded as experts in this or associated fields.

PUBLICATIONS available or to be published:

Moore T — 'Public order; the police commander's role', Policing, Vol 2, No 2, Summer 1986.

PRINCIPAL INVESTIGATOR: TONY MOORE

TITLE OF PROJECT: POLICING PUBLIC DISORDER: THE INDIRECT APPROACH

Co WORKERS: -

INSTITUTION: -

ADDRESS FOR CORRESPONDENCE:
Nursery Cottage
Crondall Road
Crookham Village
Aldershot
Hants, GU13 0SY

DURATION: January 1987 - December 1989

SOURCE OF FUNDING: Unfunded

POLICE FORCES in which research carried out: National survey and detailed research in three forces

PROJECT SUMMARY:
On the basis that there are two forms of practical experience, direct and indirect, this project seeks to examine recent outbreaks of public disorder to see how the police actually respond once serious disorder has broken out, with the intention of highlighting both successful and unsuccessful tactical manoeuvres.

METHODOLOGY:
Researching all available reports, articles and eyewitness accounts of nine outbreaks of serious disorder occurring between 1974 and 1985. Interviewing senior police officers involved in the policing of those nine outbreaks of disorder.

PUBLICATIONS available or to be published:
-

PRINCIPAL INVESTIGATOR: ROD MORGAN

TITLE OF PROJECT: A STUDY OF THE WORK OF LAY VISITORS TO POLICE STATIONS

Co WORKERS: Charles Kemp

INSTITUTION: University of Bristol

ADDRESS FOR CORRESPONDENCE:
Faculty of Law
University of Bristol
Wills Memorial Building
Queens Road
Bristol, BS8 1RJ

DURATION: October 1987 - October 1989

SOURCE OF FUNDING: Home Office

POLICE FORCES in which research carried out: National survey, 3 forces for detailed research

PROJECT SUMMARY:
An evaluation of the work of lay visitors to police stations and an examination of the procedures for their recruitment and appointment.

METHODOLOGY:
A survey of all police forces in which lay visitor schemes have been created.
Three case studies of forces with lay visitor schemes using documentary, interview and observation research methods.

PUBLICATIONS available or to be published:

Kemp C and Morgan R — Behind the front counter: lay visitors to police stations, Bristol and Bath Centre for Criminal Justice, 1989

PRINCIPAL INVESTIGATORS:	**ROD MORGAN** **Dr ROBERT REINER**
TITLE OF PROJECT:	**POLICE POWERS AND POLICIES: A STUDY OF CUSTODY OFFICERS**
Co WORKERS:	Ian McKenzie
INSTITUTION:	University of Bristol
ADDRESS FOR CORRESPONDENCE:	Faculty of Law University of Bristol Wills Memorial Building Queens Road Bristol, BS8 1RJ
DURATION:	October 1987 - October 1989
SOURCE OF FUNDING:	Economic and Social Research Council £56,480
POLICE FORCES in which research carried out:	National survey, 3 police forces for detailed investigation

PROJECT SUMMARY:
Evaluation of the role of custody officers, a pivotal aspect of the operation of the Police and Criminal Evidence Act, 1984.

METHODOLOGY:
Participant observation in several designated stations in three forces, plus analysis of police records and court cases.

PUBLICATIONS available or to be published:
-

PRINCIPAL INVESTIGATOR: **STEPHEN MOSTON**

TITLE OF PROJECT: **POLICE INTERROGATION TECHNIQUES AND SUSPECT BEHAVIOUR**

Co WORKERS: Professor Geoffrey Stephenson
Tom Williamson

INSTITUTION: University of Kent

ADDRESS FOR CORRESPONDENCE: Institute of Social and Applied Psychology
University of Kent
Canterbury
Kent, CT2 7LZ

DURATION: January 1989 - December 1989

SOURCE OF FUNDING: Home Office £25,000

POLICE FORCES in which research carried out: Metropolitan Police

PROJECT SUMMARY:
The main aim is to identify effective (and ineffective) police interviewing techniques. Unlike previous studies of interviewing techniques, background variables (eg age of suspect, sex, previous convictions, offence type, evidence, presence of support) will be controlled. This will allow detailed analyses of the effects of different interviewing techniques on outcome (eg admit/deny).

METHODOLOGY:
Survey: Detectives in seven police stations will complete a two part questionnaire for every interview they conduct. The first part, completed before an interview, assesses factors such as belief in the suspect's guilt and strength of evidence. Part 2, completed after the interview, will assess the suspect's behaviour.
Coding of interviews: Tapes of interviews will be analysed for different questioning strategies and the use of constructive and destructive tactics. Suspect responses to each technique will be analysed.

PUBLICATIONS available or to be published:
-

PRINCIPAL INVESTIGATOR: **WALTER NICOL**

TITLE OF PROJECT: **DECENTRALISATION OF OPERATIONAL AND FINANCIAL AUTHORITY IN UK POLICE FORCES**

Co WORKERS: -

INSTITUTION: University of Exeter

ADDRESS FOR CORRESPONDENCE: Centre for Police Studies
University of Exeter
Brookfield Annexe
New North Road
Exeter, EX4 4JY

DURATION: October 1988 - October 1989

SOURCE OF FUNDING: Postgraduate funding

POLICE FORCES in which research carried out: Metropolitan Police, Kent Constabulary, Cambridge Constabulary, West Midlands Police

PROJECT SUMMARY:
An examination of the decentralisation of authority, to whom, why and how.

METHODOLOGY:
Interview and document gathering.

PUBLICATIONS available or to be published:
A Brookfield Paper will be published in January 1990.

PRINCIPAL INVESTIGATOR:	**TIMOTHY O'BRIEN**
TITLE OF PROJECT:	**FOOTBALL VIOLENCE IN EUROPE, ITALY 1990**
Co WORKERS:	Kris van Linbergen (Leuven University, Belgium) Jerry Lewis (Kent State University, USA)
INSTITUTION:	Lancashire Polytechnic
ADDRESS FOR CORRESPONDENCE:	School of Health Studies Lancashire Polytechnic Livesey House Heatley Street Preston Lancs
DURATION:	April 1989 - July 1990
SOURCE OF FUNDING:	Funding applied for from the Council of Europe. Estimated £3,500 each for a team of six
POLICE FORCES in which research carried out:	Belgium, Holland, West Germany, UK

PROJECT SUMMARY:
This is a European project with researchers from Belgium, Holland, West Germany, Italy and the UK and police from Belgium, Holland and West Germany. A similar exercise was carried out in June 1988 for the European championships in West Germany.

METHODOLOGY:
Fieldwork amongst fans travelling to Italy and staying in Italy. Observation of policing methods comparisons with UK and West Germany 1988. Research into social and economic and educational background of travelling fans, through interview.

PUBLICATIONS available or to be published:

O'Brien T	Papers presented to the European Conference on Football Violence, Preston 1987
O'Brien T	'The fans' beliefs', Contemporary Psychology, January 1989
O'Brien T	'Stand Your Ground in Dusseldorf', in Euro '88 fans and hooligans, report to the Council of Europe, 1988

PRINCIPAL INVESTIGATOR: KATE PAINTER

TITLE OF PROJECT: THE HAMMERSMITH AND FULHAM CRIME AND POLICING SURVEY

Co WORKERS: John Lea
Tom Woodhouse
Professor Jock Young

INSTITUTION: Middlesex Polytechnic

ADDRESS FOR CORRESPONDENCE: Centre for Criminology
Middlesex Polytechnic
Queensway
Enfield
EN3 4SF

DURATION: July 1987 - February 1988

SOURCE OF FUNDING: Hammersmith and Fulham Council £38,000

POLICE FORCES in which research carried out: Metropolitan Police

PROJECT SUMMARY:
A household survey covering the following areas: distribution and fear of crime; precautionary behaviour; impact of crime on victims; public encounters with the police; stop and search; public assessment of police attitudes and effectiveness.
Extension of crime questions to include: racial and sexual harassment; drug abuse and other anti-social behaviour; public policing priorities; experience of and beliefs about police illegalities; stop and search; police complaints systems and opinions as to control and accountability of the police. Also multi-agency crime prevention - problems of council service delivery and demands on agencies other than police; role of victim support schemes.

METHODOLOGY:
Random household survey of entire borough (1,315 cases), plus 452 cases generated at more focused level on West Kensington Estate (Estate survey to be published separately).

PUBLICATIONS available or to be published:
The final report to be published in book form in 1989.

PRINCIPAL INVESTIGATOR:	**KATE PAINTER**
TITLE OF PROJECT	**LIGHTING AND CRIME PREVENTION** **a) THE EDMONTON PROJECT** **b) THE TOWER HAMLETS PROJECT**
Co WORKERS:	-
INSTITUTION:	Middlesex Polytechnic
ADDRESS FOR CORRESPONDENCE:	Centre for Criminology Middlesex Polytechnic Queensway Enfield, Middlesex
DURATION:	1988 - 1989
SOURCE OF FUNDING:	Thorn EMI £5,000 Philips £5,000
POLICE FORCES in which research carried out:	Metropolitan Police

PROJECT SUMMARY:
Two exploratory tightly controlled multi-agency projects looking at the impact of improved street lighting on crime, harassment and fear of crime. The projects also examine the effects of lighting on public perceptions of the environment, feelings of personal and community safety and the social usage of public space.

METHODOLOGY:
Interview surveys of pedestrians, before and after the installation of improved lighting in order to estimate incidence of crime, levels of fear and precautionary strategies employed by women to lessen their chances of attack.

PUBLICATIONS available or to be published:

Painter K	Lighting and Crime Prevention - the Edmonton Project, Middlesex Centre for Criminology, 1988
Painter K	Lighting and Crime Prevention - the Tower Hamlets Project, Middlesex Centre for Criminology, 1988

PRINCIPAL INVESTIGATORS: KATE PAINTER

TITLE OF PROJECT LIGHTING AND CRIME PREVENTION - THE HAMMERSMITH AND FULHAM PROJECT

Co WORKERS: -

INSTITUTION: Middlesex Polytechnic

ADDRESS FOR CORRESPONDENCE: Centre for Criminology
Middlesex Polytechnic
Queensway
Enfield
EN3 4SF

DURATION: 1989

SOURCE OF FUNDING: Hammersmith and Fulham Council £8,000

POLICE FORCES in which research carried out: Metropolitan Police

PROJECT SUMMARY:
This project focuses on one walkway through a sheltered housing complex. It examines the impact of improved lighting on crime and harassment with particular reference to the elderly.

METHODOLOGY:
Street survey.
Household survey.

PUBLICATIONS available or to be published:
-

PRINCIPAL INVESTIGATOR: JOHN PARKER

TITLE OF PROJECT: URBAN DESIGN, ENVIRONMENT & CRIME PREVENTION

Co WORKERS: Gillian Dawson

INSTITUTION: Greater London Consultants

ADDRESS FOR CORRESPONDENCE: Greater London Consultants
Southbank House
Black Prince Road
London
SE1 7SJ

DURATION: 1985 -

SOURCE OF FUNDING: Self-funded by Greater London Consultants

POLICE FORCES in which research carried out: -

PROJECT SUMMARY:
Series of papers - initially for NACRO, then for the Council of Europe, which are updated from other current projects. Covers primarily architectural, town planning and environmental aspects of physical urban environment.

METHODOLOGY:
Based upon actual projects and studies undertaken by Greater London Consultants, and work done by associates.

PUBLICATIONS available or to be published:

Van Soomeren P and Parker J — Crime and the Built Environment, Butterworth Architecture, 1989 (Dutch version also available).

PRINCIPAL INVESTIGATOR: ODETTE PARRY

TITLE OF PROJECT: THE EVALUATION OF ALCOHOL-RELATED CRIME PREVENTION SCHEMES IN NEWPORT, GWENT

Co WORKERS: Michael Levi

INSTITUTION: University of Wales, College of Cardiff
and
Newport Borough Council

ADDRESS FOR CORRESPONDENCE: School of Social & Administrative Studies
University of Wales, College of Cardiff
62 Park Place
Cardiff
CF1 3AS

DURATION: March 1988 - March 1990

SOURCE OF FUNDING: Welsh Office (Urban Aid)
and
Home Office PRSU

POLICE FORCES in which research carried out: Gwent Constabulary

PROJECT SUMMARY:
The research project aims to examine the link between alcohol and crime in Newport, reviews a range of possible measures to deal with some of these problems in the light of detailed crime analysis, seeks to implement some measures (after inter-agency liaison), and evaluates their impact upon alcohol-related crime.

METHODOLOGY:
Observation, interviews, and questionnaires, as well as action by the committees set up to review aspects of the problem.

PUBLICATIONS available or to be published:
-

PRINCIPAL INVESTIGATOR: GERALDINE PETTERSSON

TITLE OF PROJECT: EALING CRIME SURVEY

Co WORKERS: Bill Dixon

INSTITUTION: London Research Centre

ADDRESS FOR CORRESPONDENCE:
Bill Dixon
Police Unit
London Borough of Ealing
Civic Centre
14-16 Uxbridge Road
London W5 2HL

DURATION: March 1988 - December 1988

SOURCE OF FUNDING: Policy (Police) Sub-Committee, London Borough of Ealing

POLICE FORCES in which research carried out: Metropolitan Police

PROJECT SUMMARY:
The project was designed to survey public attitudes within the London Borough of Ealing to crime, safety and policing, residents' experiences of crime and the precautions people take against crime.

METHODOLOGY:
A total of 611 interviews were completed for the main household survey. The survey was designed to be representative of the borough as a whole. A stratified (by ward and proportion of residents born in the New Commonwealth and Pakistan) random sample of census enumeration districts was obtained. Within selected enumeration districts, a systematic random sample of 20 addresses was selected by 'Pinpoint' from the small user file of the Postcode Address List. Individual interviewees were then selected at random using the Kish method.

PUBLICATIONS available or to be published:
A summary of the findings of the main household sample and the additional survey were presented to the Council's Policy (Police) Sub-Committee. A report on the survey's findings for wider distribution will be produced in 1989.

PRINCIPAL INVESTIGATOR: KEVIN PITT

TITLE OF PROJECT: THE ECOLOGICAL PSYCHOLOGY OF THE INTERVIEW SITUATION

Co WORKERS: -

INSTITUTION: University of Durham

ADDRESS FOR CORRESPONDENCE: Department of Psychology
University of Durham
Science Laboratories
South Road
Durham DH1 3LE

DURATION: September 1988 - October 1989

SOURCE OF FUNDING: Bramshill Fellowship

POLICE FORCES in which research carried out: Cleveland Constabulary

PROJECT SUMMARY:
The focus of the research is the relationship between the interviewer/interviewee and the police interview environment. These interviews may be with a victim, witness or suspect and involve a complex system of interrelated processes, actions, decisions, influences and emotions, all of which may be affected by environmental influences. As stated, the principal concern of the research is to examine the effects of such environmental stimuli within these situations.

METHODOLOGY:
Measures of the physical aspects of the interview environments (ie temperature, lighting, humidity, room size and colour) are being compared with the perceptions of the persons using such environments, this perceptual data being obtained by means of questionnaire, cognitive mapping and personal interviews from which a model of the subject/environmental influence can be produced.

PUBLICATIONS available or to be published:
-

PRINCIPAL INVESTIGATOR: JOYCE PLOTNIKOFF

TITLE OF PROJECT: COUNCIL SERVICES TO THE VICTIMS OF CRIME

Co WORKERS: -

INSTITUTION: -

ADDRESS FOR CORRESPONDENCE:
D Cutler
Community & Police Unit
Hammersmith & Fulham Council
3rd Floor
London House
271-273 King Street
London W6

DURATION: April 1989 - October 1989

SOURCE OF FUNDING: Hammersmith and Fulham Council £8,000

POLICE FORCES in which research carried out: Metropolitan Police

PROJECT SUMMARY:
The objective of the project is to establish when victims of crime contact any part of the Council, what service(s) they require, the extent to which these needs are met, and to make recommendations for improvement of council services, with particular regard to the provision of information to the public.

METHODOLOGY:
Review of existing policy and practice re council services to victims.
Use of victim/council contact monitoring forms at council intake points (over 8 week period).
Survey of victims identified at previous stage.

PUBLICATIONS available or to be published:
-

PRINCIPAL INVESTIGATOR:	**BERNARD PORTER**
TITLE OF PROJECT:	**SECRET POLITICAL POLICING IN BRITAIN FROM c. 1790, WITH PARTICULAR EMPHASIS ON THE LONDON METROPOLITAN SPECIAL AND OTHER POLITICAL BRANCHES c. 1850-1920**
Co WORKERS:	-
INSTITUTION:	University of Hull
ADDRESS FOR CORRESPONDENCE:	Department of History University of Hull Hull HU6 7RX
DURATION:	1977 -
SOURCE OF FUNDING:	Funded from occasional research grants.
POLICE FORCES in which research carried out:	Metropolitan Police archives.

PROJECT SUMMARY:
An update and extension of previous work on the early history of the Metropolitan Police Special Branch c. 1880-1914.

METHODOLOGY:
Historical sources.

PUBLICATIONS available or to be published:

Porter B	The Origins of the Vigilant State: The London Metropolitan Police Special Branch before the first world war, Weidenfeld & Nicolson, 1987
Porter B	'The histriography of the Special Branch', Intelligence and National Security, Vol 1, 1986
Porter B	'Secrecy and the Special Branch, 1880-1914', Bulletin of the Society for the Study of Labour History, Vol 52, 1987
Porter B	Plots and Paranoia: The history of political policing in Britain, 1790 to the present day, Unwin Hyman, 1989

PRINCIPAL INVESTIGATOR:	**BARRY POYNER**
TITLE OF PROJECT:	**TASK ANALYSIS IN A POLICE DIVISION**
Co WORKERS:	Barry Webb
INSTITUTION:	The Tavistock Institute of Human Relations
ADDRESS FOR CORRESPONDENCE:	The Tavistock Institute of Human Relations 120 Belsize Lane London NW3 5BA
DURATION:	April 1988 - October 1988 (interim report)
SOURCE OF FUNDING:	Home Office PRSU £5,000 first stage
POLICE FORCES in which research carried out:	Metropolitan Police

PROJECT SUMMARY:
Developing a method for analysing the tasks of a police division so that the organisation can be continually revised to meet the changing demands through time. As a first stage to this project a list of all tasks has been prepared for the Stoke Newington Division.

METHODOLOGY:
A collaborative approach with a liaison officer and the senior management team.

PUBLICATIONS available or to be published:
An interim report is available.

PRINCIPAL INVESTIGATOR: **BARRY POYNER**

TITLE OF PROJECT: **EVALUATION OF THE EVIDENCE SO FAR EMERGING FOR CRIME PREVENTION**

Co WORKERS: Barry Webb

INSTITUTION: The Tavistock Institute of Human Relations

ADDRESS FOR CORRESPONDENCE: The Tavistock Institute of Human Relations
120 Belsize Lane
London NW3 5BA

DURATION: July 1988 - June 1989

SOURCE OF FUNDING: Leverhulme Trust

POLICE FORCES in which research carried out: -

PROJECT SUMMARY:
A review of evaluation research on all aspects of crime prevention.

METHODOLOGY:
-

PUBLICATIONS available or to be published:
-

PRINCIPAL INVESTIGATORS: **JANE PRINCE**

TITLE OF PROJECT: **ISSUES OF IDENTITY AND STRESS IN WOMEN POLICE OFFICERS**

Co WORKERS: -

INSTITUTION: Polytechnic of Wales

ADDRESS FOR CORRESPONDENCE: Department of Behavioural Science
Polytechnic of Wales
Pontypridd
Mid-Glamorgan, CF37 IDL

DURATION: 1987 - 1991

SOURCE OF FUNDING: Polytechnic of Wales

POLICE FORCES in which research carried out: Dyfed-Powys Police, South Wales Constabulary, Gwent Constabulary, West Mercia Constabulary

PROJECT SUMMARY and METHODOLOGY:
Use of type inventories to assess preferred work styles (Myers-Briggs type indicator), semi-structured interviews, questionnaires.

PUBLICATIONS available or to be published:
-

PRINCIPAL INVESTIGATOR:	**BILL PRYKE**
TITLE OF PROJECT:	**POLICE POLICIES ON CAUTIONING CANNABIS OFFENDERS IN ENGLAND AND WALES**
Co WORKERS:	-
INSTITUTION:	University of Exeter
ADDRESS FOR CORRESPONDENCE:	Centre for Police Studies University of Exeter Brookfield Annexe New North Road Exeter, EX4 4JY
DURATION:	October 1988 - October 1989
SOURCE OF FUNDING:	Bramshill Fellowship
POLICE FORCES in which research carried out:	National survey

PROJECT SUMMARY:
Survey of different criteria chosen by police forces in deciding whether to caution or prosecute possessors of cannabis.

METHODOLOGY:
Postal questionnaire and interview.

PUBLICATIONS available or to be published:
A Brookfield Paper to be published in 1990.

PRINCIPAL INVESTIGATOR: PHIL PYKE

TITLE OF PROJECT: TOLERANCE TO CRIME

Co WORKERS: -

INSTITUTION: University of Wales, College of Cardiff

ADDRESS FOR CORRESPONDENCE: Divisional Police Headquarters
Cheshire Constabulary
Kingsway
Widnes
Cheshire

DURATION: 1988-1991

SOURCE OF FUNDING: -

POLICE FORCES in which research carried out: Cheshire Constabulary

PROJECT SUMMARY:
As a result of surveys conducted during research entitled 'Unemployment and Crime', it became apparent that respondents' tolerance levels towards crime and anti-social behaviour tended to vary, not only from estate to estate, but also with regard to where that person lived on those particular estates (ie towards the centre or on the perimeter). It appeared that either because of fear of retaliation or because of imposed tolerance levels those respondents who lived towards the middle of the estates or on the upper floors of high rise dwellings tolerated more crime and anti-social behaviour than those living on the perimeters of the estates.

METHODOLOGY:
Using questionnaires, it is hoped to ascertain those factors which can cause tolerance levels to vary. In conjunction with this research a system of policing will be introduced in one of the study areas to examine and ascertain if varying methods of policing can affect an area's tolerance levels to crime.

PUBLICATIONS available or to be published:

Pyke P — Unemployment and Crime, (MSc Thesis)

PRINCIPAL INVESTIGATOR: PHILIP RAWLINGS

TITLE OF PROJECT: THE EARLY HISTORY OF THE POLICE AND POLICING IN ENGLAND AND WALES (PRE-1829)

Co WORKERS: -

INSTITUTION: University College of Wales, Aberystwyth

ADDRESS FOR CORRESPONDENCE:
Department of Law
University College of Wales
Hugh Owen Building
University College
Penglais
Aberystwyth
Dyfed, SY23 3DB

DURATION: This is a series of ongoing projects.

SOURCE OF FUNDING: Unfunded

POLICE FORCES in which research carried out: -

PROJECT SUMMARY:
A long-term series of projects looking at the emergence of a bureaucratic form of police organisation in the eighteenth century.

METHODOLOGY:
Historical - records, manuscripts, newspapers, popular literature of crime, etc.

PUBLICATIONS available or to be published:

Rawlings P — Responses to the Mid-Eighteenth Century Crime Panic, (in preparation).

PRINCIPAL INVESTIGATOR:	**PHILIP RAWLINGS**
TITLE OF PROJECT:	**'CREEPING PRIVATISATION?' THE POLICE, THE GOVERNMENT AND POLICING IN THE LATE 1980's**
Co WORKERS:	-
INSTITUTION:	University College of Wales, Aberystwyth
ADDRESS FOR CORRESPONDENCE:	Department of Law University College of Wales Hugh Owen Building Penglais Aberystwyth Dyfed, SY23 3DY
DURATION:	1988 - 1989
SOURCE OF FUNDING:	Unfunded
POLICE FORCES in which research carried out:	-

PROJECT SUMMARY:
Study of the nature of the relationship between police and government in late 1980's, focusing on way in which each sees policing and role of the police.

METHODOLOGY:
Printed sources.

PUBLICATIONS available or to be published:

Rawlings P	Papers delivered at BSA Conference, Plymouth Polytechnic, March 1989 and at conference on The Values of the Enterprise Culture, Centre for Study of Cultural Values, Lancaster University, September 1989

PRINCIPAL INVESTIGATORS: Professor DAVID REGAN

TITLE OF PROJECT: RELATIONSHIPS BETWEEN THE POLICE AND LOCAL GOVERNMENT: NON-STATUTORY POLICE ACTIVITIES IN LOCAL GOVERNMENT

Co WORKERS: Owain Mark Blackwell

INSTITUTION: University of Nottingham

ADDRESS FOR CORRESPONDENCE: Department of Politics
University of Nottingham
Nottingham
NG7 2RD

DURATION: November 1987 - November 1988

SOURCE OF FUNDING: The Rannoch Trust

POLICE FORCES in which research carried out: No police forces but a number of local authorities

PROJECT SUMMARY:
To trace the origins, history, aims, range, cost and impact of non-statutory police activities by British local authorities. The project covers the work of unofficial police committees, police committee support units, police monitoring bodies and other machinery set up or funded by local government outside the regular police committees. Particular attention would be paid to the publications produced by this non-statutory machinery.

METHODOLOGY:
Both interviews and a literature search.

PUBLICATIONS available or to be published:
-

PRINCIPAL INVESTIGATOR: Dr ROBERT REINER

TITLE OF PROJECT: CHIEF CONSTABLES: A SOCIO-LEGAL ANALYSIS

Co WORKERS: -

INSTITUTION: London School of Economics

ADDRESS FOR CORRESPONDENCE: Department of Law
London School of Economics
Houghton Street
London
WC2A 2AE

DURATION: Fieldwork 1986 - 1988
Write up currently in progress

SOURCE OF FUNDING: Nuffield Foundation £15,242
Bristol University Law Faculty Research Committee £300

POLICE FORCES in which research carried out: 40 police forces in England and Wales

PROJECT SUMMARY:
Sociological profile of the present-day chief constables in England and Wales, and analysis of their constitutional position. Detailed description and analysis of their ideologies and perspectives concerning law enforcement, order maintenance, political relations and social change. Account of their career-pattern.

METHODOLOGY:
Interviews with nearly all chief constables are main data source.

PUBLICATIONS available or to be published:

Reiner R — 'In the office of chief constable', in Current Legal Problems, Stevens, London, 1988, 135-68

Reiner R — 'Where the buck stops: chief constables' views on police accountability', in Morgan R and Smith D (eds) Coming to Terms with Policing, Routledge, 1988

Reiner R — 'Today's chief constables belong to the nation's elite', Police, August 1988 28-9.

Reiner R — Complete report will be published as a book by Oxford University Press, 1989

PRINCIPAL INVESTIGATOR: TREVOR ROBERTS

TITLE OF PROJECT: PRE-COURT DIVERSION IN WEST GLAMORGAN

Co WORKERS: -

INSTITUTION: University College of Swansea

ADDRESS FOR CORRESPONDENCE: 76a Walter Road
Swansea

DURATION: Summer 1987 - Summer 1989

SOURCE OF FUNDING: Postgraduate funding

POLICE FORCES in which research carried out: South Wales Constabulary

PROJECT SUMMARY:
The research considers the impact of recent changes in juvenile liaison procedures in West Glamorgan. It is the intention of the Constabulary to encourage the wider use of cautioning for juveniles. The research will attempt to discover whether the numbers of juveniles diverted from prosecution has increased.

METHODOLOGY:
A statistical analysis of two stages of the juvenile decision making process; the recommendations of the juvenile panels and the police decisions.

PUBLICATIONS available or to be published:
-

PRINCIPAL INVESTIGATOR: KENNETH ROBERTSON

TITLE OF PROJECT: THE STATE AND SECURITY - THE ROLE OF INTELLIGENCE IN DEMOCRATIC SOCIETY

Co WORKERS: -

INSTITUTION: University of Reading

ADDRESS FOR CORRESPONDENCE: Department of Sociology
University of Reading
PO Box 218
Reading
RG6 2AA

DURATION: 1987 - 1990

SOURCE OF FUNDING: Unfunded

POLICE FORCES in which research carried out: -

PROJECT SUMMARY:
A discussion of the role of intelligence including such issues as intelligence, Special Branch, political crime and subversion.

METHODOLOGY:
Comparative and historical; examining experience in the UK and overseas.

PUBLICATIONS available or to be published:

Robertson K G — 'Intelligence, terrorism and civil liberties', Conflict Quarterly, Vol 7, 2, Spring 1987, 43-62

Robertson K G — 'The study of intelligence in the USA', in Godson R (ed), Comparing Foreign Intelligence, Pergamon-Brassey's, 1988

Robertson K G — 'Terrorism in Northern Ireland' in Kurtz A (ed), Contemporary Trends in World Terrorism, Praeger, 1987.

PRINCIPAL INVESTIGATOR: HILARY ROE

TITLE OF PROJECT: THE EFFECTIVENESS OF LAW AS A MEANS OF COMBATING DOMESTIC VIOLENCE

Co WORKERS: -

INSTITUTION: Hull University

ADDRESS FOR CORRESPONDENCE: The Law School
Hull University
Hull HU6 7RX

DURATION: October 1987 - June 1989

SOURCE OF FUNDING: Postgraduate scholarship

POLICE FORCES in which research carried out: Norfolk Constabulary

PROJECT SUMMARY
The project is concerned with the effectiveness of the law relating to marital violence as a whole. The police as agents of law enforcement play a major role in deciding how effective the law can be and part of the research assesses how policies and attitudes of the police force in general and individual officers in particular affect how the law is put into practice.

METHODOLOGY:
Interviews with a small number of officers to give a background view rather than statistical data. Examination of figures relating to domestic assaults and local policy and methods for dealing with them.

PUBLICATIONS available or to be published:
-

PRINCIPAL INVESTIGATOR: Dr DEREK ROGER

TITLE OF PROJECT: STRESS AND STRESS MANAGEMENT IN POLICE WORK

Co WORKERS: -

INSTITUTION: University of York

ADDRESS FOR CORRESPONDENCE: Department of Psychology
University of York
Heslington
York YO1 5DD

DURATION: 1989 - 1992

SOURCE OF FUNDING: Forms part of a larger programme of research on stress and stress management.

POLICE FORCES in which research carried out: North Yorkshire Police

PROJECT SUMMARY:
The work follows from a preparatory programme of experimental laboratory work on moderator variables in stress which culminated in the construction of a scale for measuring emotional expressive style (the Emotion Control Questionnaire, ECQ). Subsequent research has shown that components of the scale are significantly associated with a variety of stress-related precursors to illness, such as elevated cortisol secretion and delayed heart-rate recovery. These and other findings led to the development of a comprehensive stress management programme, and the aim of the research is to test its effectiveness in the context of police work.

METHODOLOGY:
A prospective study which includes detailed monitoring of several outcome indices following training in stress management. Comparisons will be made between experimental and control groups, and the role of individual differences in facilitating or attenuating the effects of the programme will be investigated.

PUBLICATIONS available or to be published:

Roger D and Jamieson J — 'Individual differences in delayed heart-rate recovery following stress', Personality and Individual Differences, 9, 1988, 721-726

Roger D and Najarian B — 'The construction and validation of a new scale for measuring emotion control', Personality and Individual Differences (in press 1989).

PRINCIPAL INVESTIGATOR: **JOHN RULE**

TITLE OF PROJECT: **HENRY FIELDING AND CRIME**

Co WORKERS: -

INSTITUTION: University of Southampton

ADDRESS FOR CORRESPONDENCE:
Department of History
University of Southampton
Southampton SO9 5NH

DURATION: 1988 - 1990

SOURCE OF FUNDING: -

POLICE FORCES in which research carried out: -

PROJECT SUMMARY:
An examination of Henry Fielding, the first London Magistrate to make a serious study of crime in his Causes of the Late Increase in Robbers (1751), the first major work of English criminology.

METHODOLOGY:
Historical sources.

PUBLICATIONS available or to be published:
-

PRINCIPAL INVESTIGATOR: GRAHAM SALTMARSH

TITLE OF PROJECT: DRUGS - THE EUROPEAN DIMENSION

Co WORKERS: -

INSTITUTION: University of Exeter

ADDRESS FOR CORRESPONDENCE:
Centre for Police Studies
University of Exeter
Brookfield Annexe
New North Road
Exeter, EX4 4JY

DURATION: October 1989 - October 1990

SOURCE OF FUNDING: Postgraduate funding

POLICE FORCES in which research carried out: United States, Britain, Holland, West Germany

PROJECT SUMMARY:
An analysis of the implications for Europe of developments in drug abuse in the US.

METHODOLOGY:
Interviews, documentary search and statistical analysis.

PUBLICATIONS available or to be published:
-

PRINCIPAL INVESTIGATOR: **ANDREW SANDERS**

TITLE OF PROJECT: **LEGAL ADVICE AND ASSISTANCE TO PRISONERS IN POLICE CUSTODY AFTER ARREST**

Co WORKERS: Lee Bridges
Adele Mulvaney
Gary Crozier

INSTITUTION: Birmingham University

ADDRESS FOR CORRESPONDENCE: Faculty of Law
Birmingham University
PO Box 363
Birmingham
BI5 2TT

DURATION: October 1987 - Spring 1989

SOURCE OF FUNDING: Lord Chancellor's Department £67,000

POLICE FORCES in which research carried out: 7 police forces in England and Wales

PROJECT SUMMARY:
S.58 of PACE 1984 provides for access to legal advice for all persons detained in police stations. This research seeks to assess how well this provision is working; why the take-up rate is relatively low; the effectiveness of the various duty solicitor schemes that exist to operationalise S.58; and the impact of legal advice, when provided, on police suspects.

METHODOLOGY:
Analysis of national and regional statistics.
Creation of a data base from custody records in 10 police stations (7 police forces).
Observation of processing suspects in charge rooms etc, in 10 police stations (7 police forces).
Interview of suspects and police officers.
Study of the operation of duty solicitor schemes and interviews with solicitors.

PUBLICATIONS available or to be published:
-

PRINCIPAL INVESTIGATOR: FRANK SANDERS

TITLE OF PROJECT: POLICE DISCRETION AND THE ENFORCEMENT OF TRAFFIC LAW IN THE UK

Co WORKERS: -

INSTITUTION: University of Exeter

ADDRESS FOR CORRESPONDENCE:
Centre for Police Studies
University of Exeter
Brookfield Annexe
New North Road
Exeter, EX4 4JY

DURATION: October 1989 - October 1991

SOURCE OF FUNDING: Bramshill Fellowship

POLICE FORCES in which research carried out: Devon and Cornwall Constabulary and one other

PROJECT SUMMARY:
An examination of the effect of central policy directions on the constable's discretion.

METHODOLOGY:
Interview and questionnaire.

PUBLICATIONS available or to be published:
-

PRINCIPAL INVESTIGATOR: WILLIAM SAULSBURY

TITLE OF PROJECT: MULTI-AGENCY APPROACH TO RACIAL ATTACKS

Co WORKERS: Benjamin Bowling

INSTITUTION: Research and Planning Unit, Home Office

ADDRESS FOR CORRESPONDENCE: Research and Planning Unit
Home Office
50 Queen Anne's Gate
London
SW1H 9AT

DURATION: July 1987 - June 1991

SOURCE OF FUNDING: Home Office

POLICE FORCES in which research carried out: Metropolitan Police

PROJECT SUMMARY:
This action project is a multi-agency initiative to develop and implement a practical action project tackling racial attacks and harassment through the coordinated involvement of the London Borough of Newham, the Metropolitan Police, the Home Office, and representatives of the local community.

METHODOLOGY:
The project aims to involve all the local statutory, voluntary, and community groups concerned with racial harassment in a well defined local study area. The development, implementation, and evaluation of the action plan is intended to be a collaborative effort among these agencies. The multi-agency project will explore the application of the problem-oriented approach to this field of prevention.

PUBLICATIONS available or to be published:
-

PRINCIPAL INVESTIGATOR: Professor PHILIP SCHLESINGER

TITLE OF PROJECT: CRIME, LAW AND JUSTICE IN THE MEDIA: PRODUCTION AND CONTENT

Co WORKERS: Howard Tumber

INSTITUTION: Thames Polytechnic

ADDRESS FOR CORRESPONDENCE: Department of Film and Media Studies
University of Stirling
Stirling
FK9 4LA

DURATION: September 1986 - August 1988

SOURCE OF FUNDING: Economic and Social Research Council
£84,500

POLICE FORCES in which research carried out: Metropolitan Police
Greater Manchester Police
West Midlands Police
Merseyside Police

PROJECT SUMMARY:
This project investigates the media strategies of official and non-official bodies in the criminal justice field. It surveys crime, home affairs, and legal correspondents in the national media, and production practice in two specialised television programmes. It has analysed the content of two weeks' national press and prime time television output, and has gathered relevant data on the television audience.

METHODOLOGY:
Interviewing, observation, content analysis, audience survey analyses, documentary analysis.

PUBLICATIONS available or to be published:

Schlesinger P — 'How violent is contemporary society - some questions of interpretation', in Bonanate L (ed) The Future of Peace and the Violence of the Future, Edizioni Citta' di Lugano, 1989

Schlesinger P — 'Rethinking the sociology of journalism: source strategies and the limits of media-centrism', in Ferguson M (ed) Public Communication: The New Imperatives, Sage Publications, London, 1989,

PRINCIPAL INVESTIGATOR: Dr JOANNA SHAPLAND

TITLE OF PROJECT: POLICING ON THE GROUND

Co WORKERS: Dr Dick Hobbs

INSTITUTION: University of Oxford

ADDRESS FOR CORRESPONDENCE: Centre for Criminological and Socio-Legal Studies
University of Sheffield
430-432 Crookesmoor Road
Sheffield S10 1BL

DURATION: November 1985 - October 1988

SOURCE OF FUNDING: Economic and Social Research Council £100,000

POLICE FORCES in which research carried out: 3 police forces

PROJECT SUMMARY:
The project analyses the demand placed on the police by the public to deal with problems, incidents and disorder, and examines the response made by the police over the whole range of crime, emergencies and venue. This is used to show the priorities actually being put by the police on the different parts of their workload.

METHODOLOGY:
The same methods have been used in a subdivision of three forces. Observation and analysis of police records in the control room, at the front desk and out on patrol has led on to the following through of a sample of incidents covering ten different kinds of police work, using paper records, supplemented by observation in all relevant departments of the force and interviews with officers.

PUBLICATIONS available or to be published:

Shapland J and Hobbs D — 'Policing priorities on the ground', in Morgan R and Smith D (eds) Coming to Terms with Policing, Routledge, 1989

Shapland J and Hobbs D — Policing on the Ground in Highland, working paper available from Centre for Criminological Research, Oxford University, 1987

Shapland J and Hobbs D — Policing on the Ground in Lowland, working paper available from Centre for Criminological Research, Oxford University, 1988

PRINCIPAL INVESTIGATOR: Dr JOANNA SHAPLAND

TITLE OF PROJECT: BUSINESS AND CRIME

Co WORKERS: -

INSTITUTION: University of Sheffield

ADDRESS FOR CORRESPONDENCE: Centre for Criminological and Socio-Legal Studies
University of Sheffield
430-432 Crookesmoor Road
Sheffield S10 1BL

DURATION: November 1989 -

SOURCE OF FUNDING: Storehouse plc and other sources

POLICE FORCES in which research carried out: To be decided

PROJECT SUMMARY:
An examination of the problems of crime affecting businesses in a number of typical locations for businesses in England (the high street, shopping precincts, industrial estates, mixed residential/business areas in the inner city). Victimisation, use of police and civil courts, attitudes towards crime and crime prevention, and management policies will be covered.

METHODOLOGY:
Interviews with business people, analysis of police and other records. Interviews with police officers.

PUBLICATIONS available or to be published:
-

PRINCIPAL INVESTIGATORS: Dr ERIC SHEPHERD
Det Insp FRANK KITE

TITLE OF PROJECT: APPLICATION OF INTERACTIVE VIDEO TO INTERVIEWING AN CONTACT SKILLS TRAINING

Co WORKERS: -

INSTITUTION: City of London Polytechnic
Merseyside Police Interview Development Unit

ADDRESS FOR CORRESPONDENCE: Centre for Interview Research and Development
Department of Psychology
City of London Polytechnic
Old Castle Street
London E1 7NT

DURATION: August 1987 - ongoing

SOURCE OF FUNDING: Merseyside Police

POLICE FORCES in which research carried out: Merseyside Police

PROJECT SUMMARY:
An ongoing project aimed at introducing interactive video to sub-division/departmental level to enhance the depth and breadth of systematic 'on-the-job' training in interviewing and contact skills. Contact/interview types envisaged include: investigative interviewing, management, counselling, special needs (eg children).

METHODOLOGY:
Empirical testing of 'case study' leading to design of widely applicable/ acceptable learning framework. Methods involve knowledge elicitation from experienced experts, trainers and novices, algorithm construction and empirical testing of algorithm material.

PUBLICATIONS available or to be published:

Kite F and Shepherd E — 'Interactive video approaches to interview training', (forthcoming)

Shepherd E and Kite E — 'Training to Interview (1)', in Policing, 4, 1989, 264-280

Shepherd E and Kite E — 'Training to Interview (2)'(forthcoming)

PRINCIPAL INVESTIGATORS: Dr ERIC SHEPHERD
ANNA MORTIMER

TITLE OF PROJECT: THE COGNITIVE PROCESSES UNDERLYING INVESTIGATIVE INTERVIEWING BEHAVIOUR

Co WORKERS: -

INSTITUTION: City of London Polytechnic
Merseyside Police Interview Development

ADDRESS FOR CORRESPONDENCE: Centre for Interview Research and Development
Department of Psychology
City of London Polytechnic
Old Castle Street
London E1 7NT

DURATION: October 1988 - ongoing

SOURCE OF FUNDING: Unfunded

POLICE FORCES in which research carried out: Merseyside Police

PROJECT SUMMARY:
Examining the 'script' thinking and 'scenario' construction processes underlying police officers' behaviour in handling a case prior to the interview, during the interview and after the interview.

METHODOLOGY:
Empirical research using measures of script thinking, scenario construction, information processing and conversation management.

PUBLICATIONS available or to be published:

Shepherd E, Mortimer A and Fearns B — The cognitive processes underlying investigative interviewing, Centre for Interview Research and Development, 1989

Shepherd E, Mortimer A, and Fearns B — 'The best laid schemas', Police Review, 97, 6 January 1989, 18-19

PRINCIPAL INVESTIGATOR:	**Dr ERIC SHEPHERD** **Det Insp FRANK KITE**
TITLE OF PROJECT:	**WORKPLACE COUNSELLING IN THE POLICE SERVICE**
Co WORKERS:	-
INSTITUTION:	City of London Polytechnic Merseyside Police Interview Development Unit
ADDRESS FOR CORRESPONDENCE:	Centre for Interview Research and Development Department of Psychology City of London Polytechnic Old Castle Street London E1 7NT
DURATION:	August 1987 - ongoing
SOURCE OF FUNDING:	Unfunded
POLICE FORCES in which research carried out:	Merseyside Police

PROJECT SUMMARY:
Developing a method based on conversation management skills aimed at identifying problems, defining problems and developing solutions - centred, wherever possible on the individual's personal/psychological resources.

METHODOLOGY:
Evolving a counselling 'method' over a series of management/instructor courses, coupled into actual application of the 'method'.

PUBLICATIONS available or to be published:

Shepherd E and Kite F	'Workplace counselling in the police service'(forthcoming)
Kite F and Shepherd E	'Management conversation - conversation management' (forthcoming)

PRINCIPAL INVESTIGATORS: Dr ERIC SHEPHERD
W Det Sgt BRENDA FEARNS

TITLE OF PROJECT: INTERVIEWER MEMORY FOR DISCOURSE

Co WORKERS: -

INSTITUTION: City of London Polytechnic
Merseyside Police Interview Development Unit

ADDRESS FOR CORRESPONDENCE: Centre for Interview Research and Development
Department of Psychology
City of London Polytechnic
Old Castle Street
London E1 7NT

DURATION: February 1989 - ongoing

SOURCE OF FUNDING: Unfunded

POLICE FORCES in which research carried out: Merseyside Police

PROJECT SUMMARY:
Police interviewers must have an acceptable degree of ability to recall extended spoken text (whether from victims, complainants, witnesses or suspects) in an interview. This research seeks to examine the performance of police officers in this area.

METHODOLOGY:
Empirical testing of recall of auditory and audio-visual material.

PUBLICATIONS available or to be published:
-

PRINCIPAL INVESTIGATOR: **ANDREW SKELHORN**

TITLE OF PROJECT: **DIRECT ACTION PROTEST AGAINST BRITISH NUCLEAR WEAPONS 1945-1968**

Co WORKERS: -

INSTITUTION: Lancaster University
and
Richardson Institute, Lancaster

ADDRESS FOR CORRESPONDENCE: 9 Moss Lane
Bollington
Macclesfield
Cheshire

DURATION: 1983 - 1989

SOURCE OF FUNDING: Unfunded

POLICE FORCE in which research carried out: -

PROJECT SUMMARY:
A study of the civil disobedience wing of the protest against British nuclear weapons 1945-68 and the response of the authorities to this protest.

METHODOLOGY:
Archives of relevant organisations.
Interviews with persons involved.
Newspapers.

PUBLICATIONS available or to be published:

PRINCIPAL INVESTIGATOR: **WESLEY SKOGAN**

TITLE OF PROJECT: **BRITISH CRIME SURVEY: POLICE COMPONENT**

Co WORKERS: -

INSTITUTION: Centre for Urban Affairs, Northwestern University, Evanston, Illinois 60208, USA

ADDRESS FOR CORRESPONDENCE: Research and Planning Unit
Home Office
50 Queen Anne's Gate
London
SW1H 9AT

DURATION: September 1988 - July 1989

SOURCE OF FUNDING: Home Office

POLICE FORCES in which research carried out: National sample

PROJECT SUMMARY:
An analysis of the information in the British Crime Survey 1988 on the extent and nature of public contact with the police, satisfaction with the police and complaints against them.

METHODOLOGY:
A randomly selected sample of 4,975 residents in England and Wales were questioned about their contacts with the police. Interviews were carried out at their homes. Supplementary interviews were carried out with a sample of ethnic minorities in order to boost the numbers of Asians and Afro-Caribbeans.

PUBLICATIONS available or to be published:
Report to be published in the Home Office Research Study series.

PRINCIPAL INVESTIGATORS: DAVID SMITH

TITLE OF PROJECT: THE MAKING OF POLICING POLICY

Co WORKERS: Christine Horton

INSTITUTION: Policy Studies Institute

ADDRESS FOR CORRESPONDENCE: Policy Studies Institute
100 Park Village East
London NW1 3SR

DURATION: April 1989 - September 1991

SOURCE OF FUNDING: Economic and Social Research Council and Leverhulme Trust £147,000

POLICE FORCES in which research carried out: 4 police forces

PROJECT SUMMARY:
The study aims to describe and analyse how the various actions involved in police policy-making - the Home Office, Her Majesty's Inspectorate of Constabulary, the Home Secretary, the police authorities, pressure and community groups, political parties, the media as well as the police themselves - interact to produce changes in the style, organisation or operation of policing on the ground.

METHODOLOGY:
The research design is a comparative one, involving the analysis of three or four policy initiatives in each of three or four police forces. To provide context for the case studies, questionnaires are being mailed to all other forces, asking for details of any action they may have taken on the chosen policy initiatives.

PUBLICATIONS available or to be published:
-

PRINCIPAL INVESTIGATOR: Professor ALAN SMITHERS

TITLE OF PROJECT: GRADUATES IN THE POLICE SERVICE

Co WORKERS: Susan Hill
Geoff Silvester

INSTITUTION: University of Manchester

ADDRESS FOR CORRESPONDENCE: Department of Education
University of Manchester
Oxford Road
Manchester M13 9PL

DURATION: August 1987 - September 1989

SOURCE OF FUNDING: Charitable Foundations, university research post and police secondment £93,100

POLICE FORCES in which research carried out: National survey and detailed study in 6 forces

PROJECT SUMMARY:
The project is an independent national evaluation of the recruitment, deployment, progress and premature voluntary resignation of graduates. Issues for particular enquiry include: the numbers and distribution of graduates nationally and the reasons for variation between forces; the career aspirations of graduates and non-graduates considered in relation to deployment; promotion and wastage; the value of higher education and the need for graduates in the police service; the promotion rate of graduates compared to non-graduates; the desirability of continuing the Graduate Entry Scheme and higher education schemes for serving officers; premature voluntary resignation of graduates and non-graduates focusing on the reasons for leaving and the destinations of resignees.

METHODOLOGY:
Home Office records of serving graduate officers for the years 1971 to 1988 are analysed and a survey of all forces in England and Wales carried out through postal questionnaire. In addition, a detailed study of a sample of six provincial forces is being undertaken that includes interviews with serving and resigned officers (both graduates and non-graduates) to obtain their personal accounts. The selected forces are representative of urban, semi-rural and rural forces and vary in terms of geographical location, strength and the population per police officers.

PUBLICATIONS available or to be published:
Pilot study written up as a report for the Nuffield Foundation. (1987)

PRINCIPAL INVESTIGATOR: JIM SMYTH

TITLE OF PROJECT: SECURITY POLICY IN NORTHERN IRELAND

Co WORKERS: -

INSTITUTION: Queen's University, Belfast

ADDRESS FOR CORRESPONDENCE: Department Social Studies
Queen's University
Belfast
BT7 1NN

DURATION: -

SOURCE OF FUNDING: Unfunded

POLICE FORCES in which research carried out: -

PROJECT SUMMARY:
A study of the effectiveness of security policy in controlling arrests in Northern Ireland, and the social and political contradictions which arise from the practice of particular policies.

METHODOLOGY: -

PUBLICATIONS available or to be published:

Smyth J — 'A discredited cause?: the IRA and political violence in Ireland', in O'Day A (ed) Ireland's Terrorist Trauma, Harvester, 1989

Smyth J — Stretching the Boundaries: The Control of Dissent in Northern Ireland in Terrorism, (forthcoming)

PRINCIPAL INVESTIGATORS:	**KEITH SOOTHILL** **STEVE ACKROYD** **JOHN HUGHES** **DAN SHAPIRO**
TITLE OF PROJECT:	**THE SOCIAL ORGANISATION OF POLICE WORK AND INFORMATION TECHNOLOGY**
Co WORKERS:	Richard Harper Valerie Prince
INSTITUTION:	University of Lancaster
ADDRESS FOR CORRESPONDENCE:	Department of Sociology University of Lancaster Bailrigg Lancaster, LA1 4YL
DURATION:	November 1987 - May 1989
SOURCE OF FUNDING:	Science and Engineering Research Council and Economic and Social Research Council £24,000 Valerie Prince seconded by Lancashire Constabulary
POLICE FORCES in which research carried out:	Lancashire Constabulary

PROJECT SUMMARY:
To explore the determination of strategies for the introduction of information technology in the public service sector.
To develop guidelines to assist police authorities in deriving and implementing such strategies.
To provide the basis for further detailed studies.

METHODOLOGY:
Documentary evidence, interviews and observational work.

PUBLICATIONS available or to be published:
-

PRINCIPAL INVESTIGATORS: **PETER SOUTHGATE**
CATRIONA MIRRLEES-BLACK

TITLE OF PROJECT: **TARGETING OF TRAFFIC POLICING RESOURCES**

Co WORKERS: Dr S Stradling

INSTITUTION: Research and Planning Unit, Home Office

ADDRESS FOR CORRESPONDENCE: Research and Planning Unit
Home Office
50 Queen Anne's Gate
London
SW1H 9AT

DURATION: January 1989 - June 1990

SOURCE OF FUNDING: Home Office

POLICE FORCES in which research carried out: Hertfordshire Constabulary, Lincolnshire Police, Lancashire Constabulary, Durham Constabulary, Greater Manchester Police, West Midlands Police

PROJECT SUMMARY:
The study looks at the varying organisational structures within which traffic policing is conducted. It considers how these are related to processes for the formulation of objectives and priorities and the strategies used to carry out these objectives.

METHODOLOGY:
Interviews; observations; self-completion questionnaires; driver attitude surveys.

PUBLICATIONS available or to be published:
Report to be published in the Home Office Research Study series.

PRINCIPAL INVESTIGATORS: Dr JANET STOCKDALE
RAY WARD

TITLE OF PROJECT: PROFESSIONAL DEVELOPMENT PROGRAMME

Co WORKERS: -

INSTITUTION: London School of Economics

ADDRESS FOR CORRESPONDENCE: London School of Economics
Houghton Street
London EC2A 2AE

DURATION: - April 1989

SOURCE OF FUNDING: Metropolitan Police

POLICE FORCES in which research carried out: Metropolitan Police

PROJECT SUMMARY:
To monitor and evaluate a forcewide training programme, the Professional Development Programme, which operates at three distinct levels:-

senior officer courses	-	chief inspectors to DACs.
multi-bank course	-	constables, sergeants and inspectors (CID and uniform).
constable courses	-	constables during 3rd year of service.

METHODOLOGY:
Pre-course, end-of-course and post-course questionnaires will be applied to each of the three levels of training as appropriate.
Some post-course interviewing of students and supervisors is an option under consideration.

PUBLICATIONS available or to be published:
In-house reports only.

PRINCIPAL INVESTIGATOR: RICHARD STONE

TITLE OF PROJECT: ENTRY, SEARCH AND SEIZURE

Co WORKERS: -

INSTITUTION: Leicester University

ADDRESS FOR CORRESPONDENCE: Faculty of Law
University of Leicester
University Road
Leicester
LE1 7RH

DURATION: 1981 - ongoing

SOURCE OF FUNDING: British Academy, Leicester University Research Board £1,500

POLICE FORCES in which research carried out: -

PROJECT SUMMARY:
An examination of the means of entry available to the police, and the way in which these are used in practice. Some comparative work has been done, notably with Canada.

METHODOLOGY:
Mainly library research, using primary legal materials (cases, statutes, etc)

PUBLICATIONS available or to be published:

Stone R — Entry, Search & Seizure, Sweet & Maxwell, 1985 (2nd edition 1989)

Stone R — 'PACE: special procedures and legal privilege', Criminal Law Review, 1988, 498-507

PRINCIPAL INVESTIGATOR: JIM STOWERS

TITLE OF PROJECT: CHANGE AND THE COLONIAL POLICING SYSTEM

Co WORKERS:
Patrick Achcamdong
Abdul-Aziz Al-Alayanan
Abdul-Aziz Al-Khalifa
Nasrullah Khan
Joe Stanley
Mazrah Inayat
Muhammed Al-Fahed
Nasr Al-Masui
Asri Yusof

INSTITUTION: University of Exeter

ADDRESS FOR CORRESPONDENCE:
Centre for Police Studies
University of Exeter
Brookfield Annexe
New North Road
Exeter, EX4 4JY

DURATION: October 1987 -
SOURCE OF FUNDING: Series of MA and PhD projects

POLICE FORCES in which research carried out:
Sierra Leone
Pakistan
Bahrain
Kuwait
Ghana
Malaysia

PROJECT SUMMARY:
A comparison of overseas police forces' attempts to absorb contemporary police practices in the post-colonial era. Domestic change and international cooperation will be examined.

METHODOLOGY:
Gathering of documentation, comparative analysis, interviews.

PUBLICATIONS available or to be published:
Brookfield Papers and books from January 1990.

PRINCIPAL INVESTIGATOR:	**JAMES STURGIS**
TITLE OF PROJECT:	**THE POLICING OF THE LIQUOR LAWS IN NINETEENTH CENTURY CANADA**
Co WORKERS:	-
INSTITUTION:	Birkbeck College University of London
ADDRESS FOR CORRESPONDENCE:	Department of History Birkbeck College Malet Street London WC1E 7HX
DURATION:	1987 - ongoing
SOURCE OF FUNDING:	Original research in 1987 was funded by a Canada Research Award from the Canadian High Commission
POLICE FORCES in which research carried out:	Canadian cities - with special reference to Hamilton, Ontario

PROJECT SUMMARY:
To ascertain how well the liquor laws were enforced.

METHODOLOGY:
Archival research.

PUBLICATIONS available or to be published:

Sturgis J	Chapter in Anderson D and Killingray D, (eds) Policing the Empire, Manchester University Press, 1990

PRINCIPAL INVESTIGATOR: COLIN THOMAS

TITLE OF PROJECT: THE DEVELOPMENT OF THE BRITISH TRANSPORT POLICE

Co WORKERS: -

INSTITUTION: University of Wales, College of Cardiff

ADDRESS FOR CORRESPONDENCE: School of Social and Administrative Studies
University of Wales, College of Cardiff
62 Park Place
Cardiff, CF1 3AS

DURATION: - October 1990

SOURCE OF FUNDING: Postgraduate funding

POLICE FORCES in which research carried out: British Transport Police

PROJECT SUMMARY:
The historical development, role and accountability of the British Transport Police. Also an examination of inter-agency liaison, force objectives and issues of management.

METHODOLOGY:
Interviews and observation for contemporary information, documentary study for historical work.

PUBLICATIONS available or to be published:
-

PRINCIPAL INVESTIGATOR: Det Insp GARY THORNTON

TITLE OF PROJECT: THE PRESENT AND FUTURE ROLE OF THE CRIMINAL INVESTIGATION DEPARTMENT

Co WORKERS: -

INSTITUTION: Manchester University

ADDRESS FOR CORRESPONDENCE: Hutton Hall Police Training School
Lancashire Constabulary
Hutton
Lancs

DURATION: April 1988 - April 1989

SOURCE OF FUNDING: Bramshill Fellowship

POLICE FORCES in which research carried out: Lancashire Constabulary

PROJECT SUMMARY:
To assess present effectiveness and efficiency of CID relative to its terms of reference. Also to assess initiatives and innovations in work practice introduced in this country and abroad, to 'free up' the CID to allow it to pursue a more proactive role. Present research demonstrates detectives spend over 80% of time in the police station, less than 10% actively investigating crime. The study examines the impact of intervening variables on alleged 'poor results' - culture, multiple goal structure, use of skills, how time is spent, etc.

METHODOLOGY:
Micro study in sub-divisional headquarters, working for four months around the clock with detectives. Logging activities on a minute by minute basis. Use of self-completing logs rejected - not accurate. Subsequent detailed qualitative and quantitative analysis of all activities, strategies utilised, used of rules, impact of the Police and Criminal Evidence Act 1984 etc.

PUBLICATIONS available or to be published:
-

PRINCIPAL INVESTIGATOR:	**JOHN TIERNEY**
TITLE OF PROJECT:	**POLICING AND THE STATE**
Co WORKERS:	-
INSTITUTION:	New College Durham
ADDRESS FOR CORRESPONDENCE:	New College Durham Neville's Cross Durham City
DURATION:	1986 -
SOURCE OF FUNDING:	Unfunded
POLICE FORCES in which research carried out:	-

PROJECT SUMMARY:
Theoretical examination of the relationship between policing and the state.

METHODOLOGY:
Library based.

PUBLICATIONS available or to be published:

Tierney J	'Police discretion: raising the age of consent', Police Journal, Vol LX, No 4, Oct-Dec 1987.

PRINCIPAL INVESTIGATOR: ANNA TOLAN

TITLE OF PROJECT: THE ROLE OF THE POLICE IN DEALING WITH CHILD SEXUAL ABUSE OFFENDERS

Co WORKERS: -

INSTITUTION: Cranfield Institute of Technology

ADDRESS FOR CORRESPONDENCE:
21 Upper Road
Kennington
Oxford
OX1 5LJ

DURATION: September 1988 - September 1989

SOURCE OF FUNDING: Bramshill Fellowship

POLICE FORCES in which research carried out: Thames Valley Police

PROJECT SUMMARY:

The main purpose of the research is to highlight areas of difficulty and weakness in the police procedures for dealing with child sex abuse offenders with a view to proposing new procedures and methods of investigation.

METHODOLOGY:
Data gathering of recorded child sexual abuse cases and quantitative analysis of a large number of variables within these cases. (Data taken from one police division in Thames Valley over a period of one year.) Semi-structured interviews of police officers involved in the investigation of child sexual abuse.

PUBLICATIONS available or to be published:
-

PRINCIPAL INVESTIGATORS:	**Dr ALAN TUOHY** **Dr TONY MANSTEAD** **Dr STEVE STRADLING** **KAREN CAMPBELL** **JULIE ADAMS**
TITLE OF PROJECT:	**SOCIALISATION, SCHEMATA AND SANCTION IN ROAD-USER BEHAVIOUR**
Co WORKERS:	-
INSTITUTION:	Glasgow College Manchester University
ADDRESS FOR CORRESPONDENCE:	Karen Campbell Department of Psychology Glasgow College Cowcaddens Road Glasgow, G4 0BA
DURATION:	November 1988 - November 1990
SOURCE OF FUNDING:	General Accident £87,610
POLICE FORCES in which research carried out:	-

PROJECT SUMMARY:
Combining the approaches of cognitive and social psychology, the project examines what young drivers 'have in mind' when they drive and where these notions come from. Driving is viewed as an exercise in decision-making (adopting Hogarth's theoretical framework, 1987) and central to the theoretical analysis is one attribute of schemata, namely schemata veridicality, ie the extent to which an individual's concept of the undertaking in which he/she is engaged relates to reality.

METHODOLOGY:
The design is cross-sectional - 13, 15, 17 and 19 year old groups will be tested twice (8 months apart). Self-report measures (interviews and questionnaires) will be used and these methods will be linked to subjects' performance on interactive video.

PUBLICATIONS available or to be published:
-

PRINCIPAL INVESTIGATOR: ALISON TUPMAN

TITLE OF PROJECT: INFORMAL RESOLUTION OF COMPLAINTS AGAINST THE POLICE: COMPLAINANT AND POLICE OFFICER SATISFACTION

Co WORKERS: -

INSTITUTION: University of Exeter

ADDRESS FOR CORRESPONDENCE:
Centre for Police Studies
University of Exeter
Brookfield Annexe
New North Road
Exeter
EX4 4JY

DURATION: May 1988 - August 1989

SOURCE OF FUNDING: £6,618

POLICE FORCES in which research carried out: Devon and Cornwall Constabulary

PROJECT SUMMARY:
The project examines the following questions:
How satisfied with informal resolution are complainants and police officers? What complaints do they have? Is satisfaction/dissatisfaction linked to informal resolution procedures; to the type of event causing the complaint ?

METHODOLOGY:
Focused semi-structured interviews with 23 complainants and 35 police officers involved in informally resolved complaints 1985-1988; examination of Devon and Cornwall complaints statistics 1985-1988; interviews with members of complaints departments.

PUBLICATIONS available or to be published:
Research report September 1989.

PRINCIPAL INVESTIGATOR: Professor NORMAN TUTT

TITLE OF PROJECT: POLICE DECISION-MAKING ON JUVENILE OFFENDERS

Co WORKERS: Henri Giller
Loraine Gelsthorpe

INSTITUTION: University of Lancaster

ADDRESS FOR CORRESPONDENCE: Leeds Social Services
Selectapost 9
Sweet Street
Leeds
LS11 9DQ

DURATION: 1986 - 1987
Writing up continues

SOURCE OF FUNDING: Economic & Social Research Council
£54,000

POLICE FORCES in which research carried out: Cheshire Constabulary
South Yorkshire Police

PROJECT SUMMARY:
The project examines the influence of the Crown Prosecution Service, and particularly their juvenile specialists, on the police decision as to whether to caution, prosecute or pass for prosecution juvenile offenders admitting guilt to an offence. The project takes two police forces with different cautioning rates to examine charges.

METHODOLOGY:
Analysis of one month's sample in two police areas; tracking of the cases to examine decision-making processes.

PUBLICATIONS available or to be published:
Gelsthorpe L, Giller H and Tutt N — The impact of the Crown Prosecution Service on juvenile justice, Lancaster University, 1989

PRINCIPAL INVESTIGATOR: Professor NORMAN TUTT

TITLE OF PROJECT: USE OF APPROPRIATE ADULTS BY THE POLICE

Co WORKERS: -

INSTITUTION: University of Lancaster

ADDRESS FOR CORRESPONDENCE: Leeds Social Services
Selectapost 9
Sweet Street
Leeds
LS11 9DQ

DURATION: 1989 - continuous monitoring

SOURCE OF FUNDING: £10,000 from various local authorities

POLICE FORCES in which research carried out: -

PROJECT SUMMARY:
This is an attempt to monitor the use of appropriate adults as required under the Police and Criminal Evidence Act 1984, to see whether appropriate adults are supplied by social services, family or legal sources.

METHODOLOGY:
Recording the type of case and type of appropriate adult used in different police force areas.

PUBLICATIONS available or to be published:
-

PRINCIPAL INVESTIGATOR: HUGH TYSON

TITLE OF PROJECT: STAFFORDSHIRE POLICE ACTIVITY AND COMMUNITY ENTERPRISE (SPACE): EVALUATIONS BY POLICE AND PUBLIC

Co WORKERS: -

INSTITUTION: University of Keele

ADDRESS FOR CORRESPONDENCE: Police Station
Horninglow Street
Burton on Trent
Staffs, DE14 1BA

DURATION: April 1988 - April 1990

SOURCE OF FUNDING: Home Office PRSU £5,000

POLICE FORCES in which research carried out: Staffordshire Police

PROJECT SUMMARY:
To investigate, describe and analyse the responses of public and participants (both police and school students) to the SPACE project. To discuss the implications of the investigations and analyses for some contemporary concerns about police work.

METHODOLOGY:
Interviews with questionnaires of police officers up to the rank of inspector by random selection (10% of the force).
Interview of participants during the scheme, school students throughout Staffordshire, parents and leaders of ethnic minority (Asian) groups.

PUBLICATIONS available or to be published:
-

PRINCIPAL INVESTIGATOR: Dr PETER WADDINGTON

TITLE OF PROJECT: PUBLIC ORDER POLICING IN BRITAIN

Co WORKERS: -

INSTITUTION: Reading University

ADDRESS FOR CORRESPONDENCE: Department of Sociology
Reading University
PO Box 218
Reading
RG6 2AA

DURATION: December 1986 -

SOURCE OF FUNDING: Police Foundation £10,750

POLICE FORCES in which research carried out: Metropolitan Police (some international and other comparisons)

PROJECT SUMMARY:
To describe and evaluate changes in public order policing with reference to the growth in the use of firearms by the police, the use of specialised units and riot control equipment and tactics.

PUBLICATIONS available or to be published:
Waddington P A J — Arming an Unarmed Police, The Police Foundation, 1988
Final report due Autumn 1989
Book in preparation

PRINCIPAL INVESTIGATOR: GEOFFREY WAITES

TITLE OF PROJECT: PARTICIPANT PERCEPTIONS OF THE JUVENILE JUSTICE SYSTEM

Co WORKERS: -

INSTITUTION: University College of Swansea and Barnardos

ADDRESS FOR CORRESPONDENCE: '175' Project
175 Chepstow Road
Newport
Gwent
NP9 8GH

DURATION: June 1983 - March 1989

SOURCE OF FUNDING: Self-funded
More recently supported by Barnardos

POLICE FORCES in which research carried out: South Wales Police

PROJECT SUMMARY:
Research aims to reveal impressions of juvenile court operation in one Petty Sessional Division, in terms of harshness or leniency, and whether such impressions were shared within participant groupings (magistrates, court clerks, solicitors, police, probation, social services and education departments). Secondly, it aims to show the degree of proximity of these impressions to the facts, as reflected in a local study of the juvenile justice system.

By planning the results within an historical context, the research offers an additional insight into the apparent resistance of local juvenile justice systems to change, contained within both legislation and statements of government policy.

METHODOLOGY:
A systems study was carried out, covering 6 months of the processing of juvenile offenders. This included both decision-making and factors affecting decisions. Data was collected at both juvenile liaison and court stages. In addition, a questionnaire survey was undertaken of participants in the process.

PUBLICATIONS available or to be published:
-

PRINCIPAL INVESTIGATORS: Dr CLIVE WALKER

TITLE OF PROJECT: POLICE AND COMMUNITY IN NORTHERN IRELAND

Co WORKERS: -

INSTITUTION: University of Leeds

ADDRESS FOR CORRESPONDENCE: Centre for Criminal Justice
University of Leeds
Leeds
LS2 9JT

DURATION: May 1987 - May 1989

SOURCE OF FUNDING: Unfunded

POLICE FORCES in which research carried out: Royal Ulster Constabulary

PROJECT SUMMARY:
This project considers links between the RUC and the population in terms of Police Authority, liaison committees and otherwise. The main theme is to consider how successful those links have been or can ever be given the context of a divided society in which policing 'by consent' or at least according to British models, has proved largely unattainable.

METHODOLOGY:
Examination of relevant law and practice, documents from interested groups and a survey of attitudes and structures pertaining to policing at district council level.

PUBLICATIONS available or to be published:
-

PRINCIPAL INVESTIGATOR: SANDRA WALKLATE

TITLE OF PROJECT: RECRUIT REFERENCES AS A SOURCE OF POLICE IMAGES

Co WORKERS: Mike Brogden

INSTITUTION: Liverpool Polytechnic

ADDRESS FOR CORRESPONDENCE: School of Social Sciences
Liverpool Polytechnic
Walton House
Tithbarn Street
Liverpool 2

DURATION: November 1988 - November 1989

SOURCE OF FUNDING: -

POLICE FORCES in which research carried out: 1 police force

PROJECT SUMMARY:
Exploration of referees' conception of policing in contemporary society, by exploring the dominant themes/constructions of recruit images that appear in references in the police force.

METHODOLOGY:
Content analysis of 300 recruit references.

PUBLICATIONS available or to be published:
-

PRINCIPAL INVESTIGATOR: DAVID WALL

TITLE OF PROJECT: THE SELECTION OF CHIEF CONSTABLES IN THE POLICE FORCES OF ENGLAND AND WALES BETWEEN 1835 AND 1985

Co WORKERS: -

INSTITUTION: University of Hull

ADDRESS FOR CORRESPONDENCE: Centre for Criminology and Criminal Justice
Hull University
Hull
HU6 7RX

DURATION: October 1983 - July 1989

SOURCE OF FUNDING: Economic and Social Research Council (2 years)

POLICE FORCES in which research carried out: -

PROJECT SUMMARY:
This project examines the office of chief constable and its incumbents. Of particular interest is the development of the office of borough chief constable and the circumstances during the inter-war years which led to the selection of chief constables from the police service.

METHODOLOGY:
The analysis is based on a biographical study of the chief constables known to have held office in the boroughs and counties of England and Wales between 1835 and 1985. The data was collected from publicly available published sources.

PUBLICATIONS available or to be published:

Wall D S — 'The chief constable: a changing power structure', in Mawby R (ed) Policing in Britain, Plymouth Polytechnic, 1987.

PRINCIPAL INVESTIGATORS:	**SUE WALLIS** **Dr ERIC SHEPHERD** **THOMAS WALSH**
TITLE OF PROJECT:	**DECISION-MAKING IN AUTHORISED FIREARMS OFFICERS: EXAMINING THE ROLE OF DISTRIBUTED ATTENTION**
Co WORKERS:	-
INSTITUTION:	City of London Polytechnic
ADDRESS FOR CORRESPONDENCE:	Applied Psychology Unit Department of Psychology City of London Polytechnic Old Castle Street London, E1 7NT
DURATION:	February 1989 - July 1989
SOURCE OF FUNDING:	Unfunded
POLICE FORCES in which research carried out:	City of London Police Metropolitan Police

PROJECT SUMMARY:
Earlier work has shown that police authorised firearms officers are discriminable along two independent dimensions - yielding three characteristic patterns of AFO decision-making behaviour. This project aims to examine the value of adding a further dimension - distributed attention in a containment/seize task.

METHODOLOGY:
Micro-computer simulation; application of multivariate statistical analyses.

PUBLICATIONS available or to be published:
-

PRINCIPAL INVESTIGATORS:	**DAVID WARDEN** **RAY BULL**
TITLE OF PROJECT:	**CHILDREN AS EARWITNESSES**
Co WORKERS:	-
INSTITUTION:	University of Strathclyde
ADDRESS FOR CORRESPONDENCE:	Department of Psychology University of Strathclyde Glasgow G1 1RD
DURATION:	1989 - ongoing
SOURCE OF FUNDING:	ESRC grant applied for 2 years commencing September 1989
POLICE FORCES in which research carried out:	-

PROJECT SUMMARY:
The aim of this research is to study the process of earwitnessing in children aged 7-11 years and in adults, with particular emphasis on the interaction between auditory and visual recall, and on voice recognition.

METHODOLOGY:
Examining children's oral and written reports of staged arguments and conversations for errors of omission, commission and inference.

PUBLICATIONS: available or to be published:

Warden D and Bull R — 'Children as earwitnesses', paper presented at The British Psychological Society Annual Developmental Conference in Harlech, September 1988

PRINCIPAL INVESTIGATOR: **MOLLIE WEATHERITT**

TITLE OF PROJECT: **POLICING BY OBJECTIVES AND THE MANAGEMENT OF CHANGE: THE EXPERIENCE OF A PROVINCIAL POLICE FORCE**

Co WORKERS: -

INSTITUTION: The Police Foundation

ADDRESS FOR CORRESPONDENCE: The Police Foundation
314/316 Vauxhall Bridge Road
London SW1V 1AA

DURATION: August 1986 - 1989

SOURCE OF FUNDING: The Police Foundation

POLICE FORCES in which research carried out: Northamptonshire Police

PROJECT SUMMARY:
The research sets out to describe the implementation of policing by objectives in the force from 1981, and how the planning cycle was revised in subsequent years. It focuses on policing by objectives as a system of rational management and a (potentially rigorous) form of internal accounting. The research attempts to assess the effectiveness of policing by objectives in achieving better use of police resources and in improving managerial and operational effectiveness.

METHODOLOGY:
Review of documentary sources (force policy files); interviews with police officers, including key participants.

PUBLICATIONS available or to be published:
A report will be produced.

PRINCIPAL INVESTIGATOR: BARRY WEBB

TITLE OF PROJECT: RESEARCH INTO STREET CRIME - OFFENDER AND VICTIM PROFILES, POLICE STRATEGIES AND TACTICS

Co WORKERS: -

INSTITUTION: Cranfield Institute of Technology

ADDRESS FOR CORRESPONDENCE:
2 Oaks Way
Tattenham Corner
Epsom Downs
Surrey
KT18 5PU

DURATION: September 1988 - September 1990

SOURCE OF FUNDING: Home Office PRSU £24,000

POLICE FORCES in which research carried out: Metropolitan Police

PROJECT SUMMARY:
To carry out research into both offender and victim profiles with a view to developing effective crime prevention initiatives targeted at reducing victims' risk and developing effective intervention strategies to divert potential offenders away. Also to identify good practice as far as police strategy and tactics are concerned.

METHODOLOGY:
Review of approximately 5,000 reported incidents of street crime, to develop a framework for postal questionnaire to victims and one-to-one interviews with offenders.

PUBLICATIONS available or to be published:
-

PRINCIPAL INVESTIGATORS: BARBARA WEINBERGER
HERBERT REINKE

TITLE OF PROJECT: PUBLIC ORDER MAINTENANCE IN THE CITY: AN ANGLO/GERMAN COMPARISON

Co WORKERS: -

INSTITUTION: University of Warwick
University of Dusseldorf

ADDRESS FOR CORRESPONDENCE: Centre for the Study of Social History
University of Warwick
Coventry
CV4 7AL

DURATION: August 1988 - January 1991

SOURCE OF FUNDING: Stiftung Volkswagen £61,645

POLICE FORCES in which research carried out: Manchester Police (1890-1930)

PROJECT SUMMARY:
The project seeks to compare the priorities, decision-making process and outcomes on public order maintenance between two major industrial centres, between 1890-1930. Manchester and Wuppertal (West Germany) have been selected as the cities to be compared.

METHODOLOGY:
Comparison and interpretation of relevant criminal statistics, police organisation, local decision-making, authorities in the field of public order, and others involved in this issue (religious/philanthropic bodies etc). A systematic newspaper review.

PUBLICATIONS available or to be published:

Weinberger B E and Reinke H — 'Police perceptions of labour in the inter-war period: the case of the unemployed and of miners on strike', in Snyder F and Hay D (eds) Labour, Law and Crime: an Historical Perspective, 1987

Weinberger B E and Reinke H — Chapter in Emsley C and Weinberger B (eds), Policing Western Europe, 1850-1950, Meckler, USA (forthcoming)

Weinberger B E and Reinke H — Policing Strikes, 1906-1926, (forthcoming)

PRINCIPAL INVESTIGATOR: Chief Insp DAVID WESTWOOD

TITLE OF PROJECT: AN EXAMINATION OF THE RELATIONSHIP BETWEEN SOCIAL STRESS AND CRIME

Co WORKERS: -

INSTITUTION: Bristol Polytechnic

ADDRESS FOR CORRESPONDENCE: Department of Economics and Social Sciences
Bristol Polytechnic
Coldharbour Lane
Frenchay
Bristol, BS16 4QY

DURATION: October 1985 - September 1989

SOURCE OF FUNDING: Initially funded by Somerset Constabulary and principal researcher
Home Office PRSU £22,500

POLICE FORCES in which research carried out: Avon and Somerset Police

PROJECT SUMMARY:
The purpose of the research is to explore the links between recorded social stress indications and the decision-making process in the police in respect of offenders. It is intended to determine what factors tend to lead to a police decision to caution or prosecute an offender, from interview and observation and to relate these results to the presence or absence of the factors identified in urban and rural areas of Avon.

METHODOLOGY:
The first stage involved the selection and coding of a sample of detected crime for the year 1981, and converting this into an area/offender-based data set. The second involves in-depth questionnaire based interviews with a stratified sample of police officers and young adults. Once decision-making factors have been identified, they will be compared with the data set to determine whether they result in an amplification effect.

PUBLICATIONS available or to be published:

Westwood D — An analysis of the effects of differential prosecution practices in the context of social class, Bristol Polytechnic Occasional Papers in Sociology, No 5, 1987

PRINCIPAL INVESTIGATOR:	**PHILIP WHITTICK**
TITLE OF PROJECT:	**TECHNOLOGY AND ITS EFFECT UPON THE INVESTIGATION OF, AND PRESENTATION OF EVIDENCE IN SERIOUS FRAUD CASES**
Co WORKERS:	-
INSTITUTION:	Southampton University
ADDRESS FOR CORRESPONDENCE:	Det Supt A B Whittick PT4 Branch New Scotland Yard Broadway London, SW1
DURATION:	January 1988 - February 1989
SOURCE OF FUNDING:	Bramshill Fellowship
POLICE FORCES in which research carried out:	Fraud squads in England and Wales

PROJECT SUMMARY:
An investigation of the effects of technology on the investigation and presentation of evidence in serious fraud cases.

METHODOLOGY:
Survey of fraud squads by questionnaire.
Reading of source papers.

PUBLICATIONS available or to be published:
-

PRINCIPAL INVESTIGATORS: Professor PAUL WILES
Professor TONY BOTTOMS (University of Cambridge)

TITLE OF PROJECT: COMMUNITIES AND CRIME IN SHEFFIELD

Co WORKERS: Ann Hollingworth

INSTITUTION: Sheffield University

ADDRESS FOR CORRESPONDENCE: Centre for Criminological and Socio-Legal Studies
Sheffield University
430-432 Crookesmoor Road
Sheffield S10 1BL

DURATION: June 1987 - December 1988

SOURCE OF FUNDING: Home Office £84,000

POLICE FORCES in which research carried out: South Yorkshire Police

PROJECT SUMMARY:
A re-examination of crime and offending patterns in six small residential areas of Sheffield, twelve years after previous detailed research. The areas of interest were originally chosen as three matched pairs, comprising one pair of council high-rise estates, one pair of council pre-war housing estates and one pair of areas of predominantly privately rented housing. Each pair was matched to control for population characteristics (social class, age, sex, etc) and areas were selected to provide, within each pair, one area high on official measures of crime and one area low on such measures. Thus comparisons could be drawn between areas which were similar in terms of population, design of housing and tenure, but which differed in extremes of criminal activity.

METHODOLOGY:
It is intended to collect again the official police data concerning all the areas, and to rerun a modified and updated version of the survey, to investigate any changes in crime rates and relative crime rates between the areas. Data will be collected from the Sheffield City Council housing department, both to discover changes in the housing allocation process and to obtain measures of current resident turnover and popularity of the various council estates. The social history of the six areas over the twelve year period will also be investigated as a key to understanding change. Residents' self-report data on victimisation, collected by means of a survey, confirmed the crime differences shown in the official data.

PUBLICATIONS available or to be published:

PRINCIPAL INVESTIGATORS: Det Sgt BRYAN WILLIAMS
Dr ERIC SHEPHERD

TITLE OF PROJECT: THE PSYCHOLOGY OF INTERVIEWEE DISCLOSURE

Co WORKERS: -

INSTITUTION: Merseyside Police Interview Development Unit
City of London Polytechnic

ADDRESS FOR CORRESPONDENCE: Interview Development Unit
Merseyside Police Training Centre
Mather Avenue
Liverpool
L18 9TG

DURATION: August 1989 - ongoing

SOURCE OF FUNDING: Unfunded

POLICE FORCES in which research carried out: Merseyside Police

PROJECT SUMMARY:
An examination of the potential psychological basis for an interviewee's decision to disclose or not to an interviewer. Also to examine the fine grain behavioural exchange of the interview to identify disclosure decision-making.

METHODOLOGY:
Interviews, questionnaires, analysis of case simulations and actual cases

PUBLICATIONS available or to be published:
Shepherd E and Williams B 'Something to Hide?', Police Review, 10 March 1989, 498-499

PRINCIPAL INVESTIGATOR: Inspector SUSAN WOOLFENDEN

TITLE OF PROJECT: POLICE ABSENTEEISM: ITS MEANING, MEASUREMENT AND CONTROL

Co WORKERS: Alan Trickett
Gillian Steward

INSTITUTION: University of Manchester

ADDRESS FOR CORRESPONDENCE: Personnel Department
Merseyside Police
PO Box 59
Liverpool
L69 1JD

DURATION: April 1988 - September 1989

SOURCE OF FUNDING: Home Office PRSU £6,400.

POLICE FORCES in which research carried out: Merseyside Police

PROJECT SUMMARY:
The aim of the project is to identify those factors most closely associated with absence at both an individual and organisational level and to provide an overview of absence in the force. The data made available will provide management information which is essential if the problem is to be effectively addressed.

METHODOLOGY:
Information on a range of personal and organisational factors in respect of each officer in the force, together with comprehensive details of their sickness absence during a 12 month period (1.8.88 - 31.7.89), is being collected. This information is subsequently analysed using SPSS. Variations in sickness notes in respect of each of the factors examined and between specific groups of officers are identified.

PUBLICATIONS available or to be published:
Interim report (1st 6 months data) available from PRSU.

PRINCIPAL INVESTIGATOR: ALAN WRIGHT

TITLE OF PROJECT: DRUG ENFORCEMENT STRATEGIES IN UK DRUG SQUADS AND DRUG WINGS

Co WORKERS: Alan Waymont
Frank Gregory

INSTITUTION: Southampton University

ADDRESS FOR CORRESPONDENCE: Department of Politics
Southampton University
University Road
Highfield
Southampton SO9 5NH

DURATION: 1987-1989

SOURCE OF FUNDING: Police Foundation £28,800

POLICE FORCES in which research carried out: National survey

PROJECT SUMMARY:
The project under the auspices of the National Drugs Intelligence Coordinator and ACPO Crime Committee seeks to describe and classify the variety of enforcement strategies deployed against drug abusers and traffickers in the UK. The role of centralised intelligence systems in strategies and on performance is assessed on the basis of operational perceptions. Summary results will be publishable but for obvious reasons, detailed data will not be made available to the general public.

METHODOLOGY:
Telephone surveys, existing records, interviews within a quota sample of forces and units to maximise (on theoretical grounds) critical between-unit variance.

PUBLICATIONS available or to be published:
A report will be produced, restricted to summary accounts at the discretion of the relevant authorities.

PRINCIPAL INVESTIGATOR:	**WISSAM YOUSIF**
TITLE OF PROJECT:	**A REVIEW OF INFORMATION TECHNOLOGY AIDS TO THE INVESTIGATION OF CRIME.**
Co WORKERS:	-
INSTITUTION:	University of Exeter
ADDRESS FOR CORRESPONDENCE:	Centre for Police Studies University of Exeter Brookfield Annexe New North Road Exeter, EX4 4JY
DURATION:	October 1986 - June 1989
SOURCE OF FUNDING:	Postgraduate funding
POLICE FORCES in which research carried out:	Devon and Cornwall Constabulary

PROJECT SUMMARY:
A review of the state of police information technology in the UK plus an examination of current investigation practices and innovative projects, including the Bayes project.

METHODOLOGY:
Primarily a gathering together and analysis of documents.

PUBLICATIONS available or to be published:

PRINCIPAL INVESTIGATOR:	**MICHAEL ZANDER**
TITLE OF PROJECT:	**CONFISCATION OF ASSETS**
Co WORKERS:	-
INSTITUTION:	London School of Economics
ADDRESS FOR CORRESPONDENCE:	London School of Economics Houghton Street London WC2A 2AE
DURATION:	1989
SOURCE OF FUNDING:	Police Foundation £5,000
POLICE FORCES in which research carried out:	-

PROJECT SUMMARY:
A review of the American antecedents of the Drug Trafficking Offences Act with special reference to procedures for confiscation of assets and their use in drug enforcement. Comparison of UK and US legislation.

PUBLICATIONS available or to be published:

Zander M	Confiscation and Forfeiture Law: English and American Comparisons, The Police Foundation, 1989

SUBJECT INDEX

F

INSTITUTION INDEX